WHITE ... SSIAN S.S.R. ... UNION OF SOVIET SOCIALIST R...

Gomel ... Kursk ... Stary Oskol

Shostka ... Kharkov

KIEV ... Radomyshle ... Poltava ... KRASNOGRAD

DNEPROPETROVSK ... MAKEYEVKA

ZNAMENKA ... S.S.R. ... STALINO

Proskurov ... K R A I N I A N ... DNEPRODZERZHINSK

DOLINOVKA

MOLDAVIAN S.S.R. ... Zhdanov

Nikolaev ... Azovskoe More (Sea of Azov

ODESSA

Romaл ... CRIMEA Krymski Poluostrov

N I A

BUCHAREST

ACAL ... PRISON ROUTE ⅢⅢ ⅢⅢ ESCAPE ROUTE ••••••••

SCALE OF MILES: ONE INCH EQUALS
APPROXIMATELY 106 MILES ... C K ... B A ... L

AIR DISTANCE MAKEYEVKA TO BERLIN: 1,120 MILES ... S

Turnavo

GARIA

BORDERS AS IN 1957

P9-APX-989

THE SEVENTH ESCAPE

by Jan Doward

PACIFIC PRESS PUBLISHING ASSOCIATION

Mountain View, California   Omaha, Nebraska

THE SEVENTH ESCAPE

To

Walter and Irma

for the inspiration of their friendship

and to David

for helping to make the writing

of this story a success.

Library of Congress Catalog Card No. 68-54399

Preface

Like millions of other Europeans, Walter Logé was caught in the violent vortex of World War II. An ambulance driver in the German army, he was taken prisoner toward the end of the conflict and shipped by boxcar deep into Russia to the gloomy labor camp of Makeyevka.

But Logé's indomitable spirit rose above it all, because he was a remarkable man who looked at the world through kindly eyes, who empathized with peasants, guards, soldiers—nearly everyone. All kinds of people, whether German, Romanian, or Russian, were his friends. Though a German himself (with a French surname inherited from Huguenot ancestors), he could strike up a tune on the Russian balalaika and watch the light come back into the eyes of a yardful of gaunt, discouraged prisoners as they began to sing and clap their hands. While in a state of near starvation, he could still joke with his captors: "Why do I want to work in the kitchen? That's where they keep the food, isn't it? " And what other German prisoner just escaped from a coal mine ever marched along a country road with a passel of Russian peasant girls singing the Sunday School song, "Always Cheerful"?

Though a pleasant and gentle man, with an almost child-like faith in the goodness of God and in the innate decency of men, Logè owned nerves of Swedish steel, lightning-fast wits, and an incredible determination to escape and somehow cover the many hundreds of miles across the reaches of the Ukraine and Poland westward to Berlin, where his beloved wife and three children awaited him— if they were still alive.

This is not just another war story, or merely another chapter in the long, bitter story of man's inhumanity to man. It is not told to work off a grudge. (Happily the Stalinist labor-camp era is long past.) It is not simply a dreary chronicle of misery and brutality, nor is it written to remind us that war brings suffering to the innocent and arouses the worst of human passions.

Rather, it is a document of human freedom and brotherhood. It is more than a book; it is an experience. To follow Walter Logé on his desperate, but at times humorous, flight from degradation and slavery is a heartwarming adventure of the human spirit.

THE PUBLISHERS.

Contents

THE bulging troop train pulled away from the Vienna station without bands, farewells, or fanfares. Only the SS men seemed alert and interested, as their trained eyes scrutinized the thronged depot for possible deserters. They stood on the platform with their thumbs tucked under their belts, watching.

Walter Logé, stocky, broad-shouldered, with a far-from-French square jaw and close-cropped dark-brown hair, leaned back in his seat to relax. He tried not to look too obviously pleased with himself, but he had accomplished all he had intended to do. With just a standby leave from the military hospital, where he had been convalescing from

The Camp at Caracal

acute arthritis, he had made a rush trip to Berlin to visit his wife, Irma, and their three children, Ursel, Dieter, and Doris. And no one had noticed his absence. Not even Himmler could have traced his movements. He had arrived in Vienna in time to receive the inspection stamp in his passbook, with four hours of sight-seeing time before catching the noon train for the eastern front.

Walter had participated in the initial 1941 drive into Russia. As a medical corpsman with the Wehrmacht he had witnessed the horrors this campaign produced—the masses of torn, twisted bodies of soldiers and civilians caught in the violent death of the blitzkrieg, the scorched-earth policy of the retreating Russians, and once the fantastic annihilation of an entire Red contingent. Those soldiers, unearthly, wide-eyed, were dead at their posts, frozen in their positions by concussion bombs. The latter event could never be erased from Walter's memory. He could see those men yet, like statues with guns ready.

Although he had never dared express himself, even then he had sensed that the day would come when the Germans would be driven back across those vast plains. Now his mind quickly took in the past few years—the severe winters, the spring mud, the final retreat from Stalino, the regrouping and preparations in France, the convalescing from wounds. And now he was to rejoin his unit—if he could find it. It might have been caught in the Crimean squeeze. From news filtering back, he assumed that the Germans were in full rout.

Logé slumped a little in his seat and pulled his cap over his eyes, adjusting himself as best he could for a rest. The train was warm, for this was a summer day. But he had learned to make himself as comfortable as possible in crowded quarters. In days ahead he might not be as well off as this. Time seemed to stand still. The steady clicking of wheels over the rails had a somnolent effect, and Walter was only dimly conscious of the passing of an afternoon and a night.

Suddenly the train jerked to a halt. Peering into the gray dawn, the passengers watched the shadowy figures of the Romanian troops awaiting the German trains from Vienna. This must be Peshti, end of the line.

Maybe the end of the line in another sense too, Walter reflected. This was Tuesday, August 22, 1944.

The new arrivals were herded into trucks and transported to an airfield on the outskirts of Bucharest. Officers and men kept probing the Romanians about the situation, but either they had forgotten German or they knew too much to answer any questions. Two days later, on August 24, Romania officially declared war on Germany.

For a week the Germans were forced to forage for ripening watermelons in nearby fields. Hiding in ditches and culverts, they protected themselves from incessant bombings by the Allies, who seemed to care little about Romania's decision so long as there were Germans to destroy. The new contingent from Vienna was joined by those fleeing the advancing Reds. It was a motley group: sailors from the Black Sea region, officers and men from the bedraggled segments of the Wehrmacht that had escaped the Crimea and the Ukraine, and a few grounded Luftwaffe personnel who were feeling the foot soldier's problems for the first time. It was hard to conceive this war-weary mixture as belonging to the Nazi forces that had goose-stepped through conquered cities. No longer did jackboots echo along cobblestone streets. Now the Nazi troops did not march; they shuffled. Broken in spirit, these hollow-eyed men simply waited for someone to give the command that they hoped would end the nightmare.

A command was not long in coming. The Romanians set

up loudspeakers and announced that all German personnel were to move northward toward the Siebenburgen sector. Small knots of Germans clustered about the speakers listened incredulously to the next part of the announcement.

"Free passage will be provided back to your homeland."

What was happening? Was the war over? What about the advancing Reds? The questions came, but the answers really did not matter. There was no choice. Judging by the stream of retreating Germans, the Russians must be advancing at a terrible rate. To await them meant annihilation or slavery. Long columns of men began forming and moving in the direction the Romanians had indicated.

Local villagers who were still pro-German welcomed the marchers with banners, cheers, food, and wine. Perhaps, thought the dazed soldiers, the horrors of it all were really over. Finally laying down their arms and placing them in a warehouse, as directed by the Romanians, they boarded waiting trains. Hope slowly revived. Maybe the war had ended and they were really going home.

The Romanians kept their bargain of a "free passage," but during the night the soldiers sensed a shift in direction. Instead of heading toward Germany the trains traveled southward, and by dawn the Germans were being herded into the former Romanian army camp at Caracal on the Bulgarian border. When the great wire gate shut behind them, they knew they had been tricked.

Shafts of morning sunlight slanted through the thick dust that rose as 4,000 prisoners milled in the compound. It choked the men and caked their nostrils. Unless a wind arose, relief seemed impossible. But hanging heavier than the stifling air was dread and foreboding. No wind could clear this. Its apprehensive weight hung like a shroud over the whole encampment.

Ordinarily Walter Logé was the kind of man who could

rise above any despondency, but now even he could think of little that was encouraging. He had visited Russian peasants' homes and played the balalaika for the conquered, when fraternizing and singing with Russians was really not on the Nazi agenda. He had laughed and joked while recuperating from wounds in an army hospital, knowing that when he was strong enough he would be sent back to the front. He had dodged the Gestapo to bring cheer to his wife and three children in Berlin at a time when there was little hope of ever seeing them again. But the present situation seemed different, and it was really getting through to him. He felt not so much fear, only a sense of hopelessness. The uncertainty of how his family would make it through the terrible Allied raids, and the certainty of his own slavery— he felt his usual optimism buckling under the strain. He sat down with a dozen other men in one of the corners nearest the railroad tracks and stared through the three rows of barbed wire. For several minutes no one spoke.

Finally Walter began deliberately, as if every word had to be weighed. "You see those railroad cars? They'll be hauling us to Russia one of these days. Maybe to Siberia for all we know."

Another soldier leaned forward and shook his head. "I doubt that. We'll be put to work in a coal mine right here in Romania."

The others seemed to agree. The Romanians needed the Germans to work their own mines. Why should they be sent to Russia?

"Just wait. We may not be riding on that particular train, but someday soon we'll be shipped to Russia right from that spot." Logé pointed a forefinger toward the cars.

For a moment he looked once more at the railroad cars. His squat, husky body outlined against the barbed wire gave him the appearance of someone who would be hard to hold. Obviously he was capable of tremendous endurance. He started to turn away from the men and then stopped. He wanted to have a last parting word.

"I have a hunch the Reds will be here sooner than we think."

With this Walter made his way across the crowded compound toward the barracks. He might find an empty bunk and get away from the dust.

It took a moment for the soldier-prisoner's eyes to adjust to the dim interior. The Romanians had not been lavish with windows, and the whole place had a dingy appearance about it. Slowly Walter had to make his way between the rows of bunks, trying to find one that might have a mattress or even a little straw.

While the barracks had looked empty at first, Logé now could make out a pair of crutches protruding from the lower right-hand bunk nearest the door at the other end. As he approached, he saw a figure lying face up on the bare bunk boards. He made out a lean, sharp-featured man with a very short haircut. From the blue-gray uniform and insignia Logé knew immediately that this was a Luftwaffe officer.

Instinctively Walter bent over the man. "Sir, I'm a medic. Is there anything I can do for you?"

The officer's eyes slowly opened, and he turned his head slightly to see the speaker. "Yes— Yes— A free passage back to Berlin."

Logé smiled slightly. "Sir, if you find it let me know. That's my home too."

Grimacing with pain, the officer raised himself on his left elbow to face the soldier, and introduced himself: "Alfred Mattern."

"Walter Logé."

"Sounds French." Mattern groaned as he lay down again, but there was a slight twinkle in his eyes. "A Frenchman with a Berlin accent."

Walter sat down on the lower bunk across from him. "Not a Frenchman, really. A line of Logés came from the Huguenots when they fled the persecutions in France several centuries ago. Now there's been enough mingling of good German blood to make me love sauerkraut."

They both laughed, but the laughter quickly died.

"It's good to laugh," said Alfred. "Good if you can."

Walter leaned his head against the bunk post. "There's not much to laugh about now. The Reds will be here shortly, and it's doubtful we'll ever get back to Berlin."

Berlin. The name caused the men to reminisce. Their conversation ebbed and flowed from the past to the present in a shifting tide of recollections.

"Before the war I received my training in electronics with the Telefunken Company in Berlin." Alfred obviously spoke with a sense of pride and accomplishment. "I specialized in high-tension installations—mainly industrial, you know—commercial radio transmitters, high voltage transmission, and emergency power cutoffs."

Walter did not know. This was all esoteric to him, but he noticed the way Alfred's eyes brightened.

"I hold a master's degree as an electrical engineer and electrotechnician."

"Just what did all that have to do with the Luftwaffe?" Walter wanted to know.

"Nothing, really. They needed pilots and gave me the training, that's all. It's too bad I didn't get into something else—something closer to my former work. Then this probably wouldn't have happened." Alfred pointed a finger toward his back. "I injured my spine when my plane was shot down near Bucharest. I was about fifty feet off the ground when the Romanian artillery got me. They tell me I'll never walk again without crutches."

In spite of the pain whenever he moved, Alfred wanted to face Walter. As he rolled sideways their eyes met in mutual understanding.

"But I will walk again. I will walk without crutches, I promise you."

Walter thrust his square jaw forward as if to punctuate Alfred's own determination. "You can do anything if you set your heart to it. Once in the late 30's, when I was still a painter, they told me I would die of lead poisoning. I just changed jobs—drove an ambulance for the DRK [German Red Cross] and decided I was going to live anyway."

Walter stood up. Planting his feet apart, he looked down at Alfred. "I tell you, when a man sets his heart to a thing, he can do it even though everyone else may say it is impossible. I believe you can walk again."

Within two weeks the Russians appeared at the main gate just as Walter Logé had predicted. Methodically they began sorting the prisoners for the first shipment eastward. Silently the prisoners watched as hundreds of their comrades were marched off to slavery. What horrors and hell waited for these men none could tell, but those remaining caught a glimpse of their own fate.

There was not a prisoner in the whole camp at Caracal who did not wish the Russians would let the Romanians run things themselves. From the consistent friendliness of the Romanian guards they knew their former Axis partners still retained a soft spot for them. The guards indicated that they feared their giant eastern neighbor as much as did the Germans.

Throughout the autumn of 1944 the Russians continued to trim the prisoner ranks until by late November only a thousand or so remained. Whenever the Reds marched off a new crop Walter would check to see if his friend Alfred Mattern was still in the barracks.

"Good," he would say each time. "Good—we are still together."

They both knew, however, that this kind of luck couldn't last. In time they would both leave the Caracal camp for something far worse. Neither of the men talked about it anymore. They found life more bearable to accept each day as it came, refusing to borrow from the future.

The brightest spot for every prisoner was the moment when members of the DRK visited the camp and promised to deliver a three-word message for each man. Irma Logé had repeatedly said she could stand the incessant bombings and the terrible uncertainty of each moment with her three children in Berlin, but the persistent pressure of not knowing the whereabouts of her husband tormented her to the quick. Did he ever reach his unit? Was he killed in the onslaught of the advancing Reds? Buried somewhere in an unmarked grave? Taken prisoner? When the DRK delivered those three words on November 28, "Well Internment Walter," he knew his wife would lift her tear-stained face in a prayer of thanksgiving and exclaim, "My Walter is alive! He is alive!"

She could not know where he was, but she would not lose hope. Her deeply religious nature perceived the hand of Providence in all that happened. Those few hours of his secret visit in Berlin before leaving for Vienna, she had said, probably made the difference. If he had reached his unit, she was sure widowhood would have been hers. No one could argue with her. From the fragments of news she had gleaned, Walter's unit was apparently wiped out.

The DRK permitted a twenty-five word reply, but for some reason Walter received none. It would have brought much cheer to him, but his indomitable spirit maintained a

2—S.E.

high level anyway. He simply would not permit himself to slump into a state of despair as many prisoners did.

In the meantime the first word of his message home was no longer applicable. He had a sudden recurrence of his old arthritic malady. He spent a week in the prison hospital.

A few days after his return to the compound it looked as if he should have stayed a little longer. Around mid-morning five Russian officers walked through the main entrance carrying a submachine gun and began to round up the remaining prisoners. The Germans were puzzled. Not a train was in sight, but the Russians made it clear that this group was expected to walk—walk all the way to slavery. There might be a train somewhere, but all must walk or be shot on the spot.

Walter knew enough Russian to understand their method of counting. It was to be 100 men to a row, ten rows deep. As the officer in charge began counting "Raz, Dva, Tri . . .," Walter moved farther to the rear. He needed time to think.

"I can't walk very far, not now," he said to himself.

And there was no time to hunt up Alfred for consultation. He moved as far back as he could without being noticed. While the men lined up, he quietly prayed.

The Nazis had hoped to stifle all religious faith, attempting to convert the nation to their own brand of religion. Walter Logé had been one of those unwilling to go along. He had kept alive his faith as countless others had done during Hitler's rise to power. Now he needed the reassurance that God would be with him. It came—and with it a plan.

Fumbling in his pocket for his Red Cross armband, he slipped it into place and waited. He must time this perfectly. He watched until an officer swung the twenty-five-foot gate inward and the prisoners began marching through. Under the watchful eyes of the armed Russians an attempted break on the part of anyone would have been suicide. He must wait for the moment. His heart began to pound. This had to look natural.

As the last few rows started through, Logé made his move. Striding forward as if he were in charge, he walked up to the last Russian officer and stayed with him until he was even with the gate. Whatever the pains in his knees, he must not stop now. Grasping the end of the gate, he swung it closed just after the officer passed through. The Russian turned around and glanced at him as he shut it and dropped the bolt in place.

For a moment their eyes met. Snapping to attention, Walter gave a salute and then did an about-face. The last thing he wanted was an interrogation. As he walked briskly back toward the barracks he felt hot all over. He expected to hear the command to return, but none came.

Alfred Mattern was in the same barracks with all the other injured, and Walter headed there immediately. He startled the ten remaining men with his quick entrance. Slamming the door behind him, he announced, "I have returned to take care of you. Remove your bandages. I must see your wounds."

Alfred raised his head to see what his friend was doing. "Why the sudden interest in wounds, Walter?"

"Never mind. I'll look at your back in a moment too."

The men quickly caught the gist of what was happening. As he passed down the line Walter ordered, "Keep calm. It is important that I take care of you."

When he reached Alfred he gave him a pat on the shoulder. "How's the back?"

Alfred gave him a knowing smile.

Walter leaned forward and whispered. "It was close. I'll tell you about it later."

After a few minutes Walter looked through one of the windows to see if anyone was coming. There was not a sign of life in the camp. He went to another window and peered out. Still no evidence. He stepped outside and cautiously looked around. Finally he walked all the way around the compound area. To his astonishment there was not a Russian or Romanian in sight. He was alone with ten injured men. He hurried back to the barracks.

"There's not a guard anywhere," Walter said breathlessly.

Alfred looked surprised. "You're joking!"

"No, I'm not. They're all gone—vanished."

"Maybe the Romanians thought they got the whole lot of us."

Walter nodded.

Alfred started to speak again, but Walter held up his hand.

"I know what you are going to say."

He paused and looked at the others who were listening to every word. "I'm not going. It would be easy, and I know you'll call me a fool, but I'm not. I can't leave you and the others. Not now; not without someone to take care of you."

A long silence followed. At last Alfred spoke. "You should really make an attempt."

"No! Now please—"

"This is your best possible moment of escape. You'll never be closer to home."

Walter shook his head No.

A slight moisture filmed the ex-flier's eyes. "Now I know for sure your actions were not a ruse for the Russians," Alfred said.

Six hours later the Romanians returned. Walter Logé went directly to them and announced his intentions of taking care of the remaining men. He would need medical supplies immediately. The guards seemed pleased and promptly honored his request by bringing a box from the hospital. Whatever thoughts may have been entertained, they never openly questioned his assumed leadership. They watched with obvious satisfaction his diligence in attending to the men and seemed glad for his presence.

Several days later the whole camp was crowded again, this time with civilians. The Reds had ordered all those of German descent living in Romania to be interned. The authorities, however, had no intention of crowding the camp beyond its capacity. There was to be a separation. And it was this that tore at the hearts of the men who saw it. Every man remaining in the barracks had known hard action and had witnessed many heartrending sights since the war began, but this touched even the most seasoned soldier.

Parents were forced to remain within while children were escorted outside with the grandparents. The latter were told to take the children home and care for them. The Reds wanted only the men and women for their slave labor. It would have been pathetic during any season, but the early part of December had brought real winter weather, and the sight of the little ones kneeling in the snow crying and begging to be with their parents haunted the memories of those who saw it. Many mothers fell prostrate by the barbed wire as they saw the guards take away their babies. Slowly the whole group on the outside were prodded and pushed along. At last only the scattered tracks of the very old and the young, where they had crossed the camp cemetery, remained in view. For days Caracal resounded with bitter cries and wails of the parents.

Logé had been so successful with securing medical supplies that he pressed the guards to bring in any musical instruments they could find. "We must do something to bring a little cheer. Music is good for everyone."

He told them he could organize a little band and entertain the people during the long evenings. The guards said it sounded like a good plan. They would like to have something to liven up their own boring situation. It didn't take long for the Romanians to scrounge around Caracal for anything that could be plucked, scraped, blown, or beaten —anything to make music.

In the meantime Mattern had another idea. Why not get a shortwave set going? Getting the news would be a good morale builder too. The guards balked at this. They were under constant surveillance by the Russians. Music was one thing, but a radio might mean trouble.

"You've been so successful with them," Alfred told Walter, "why not tell them we could use the music to drown out the radio? I could listen and then safely hide the set if the Russians return. I could relay the news after every performance."

It worked. The last thing the Romanians wanted was to have the Russians down their throats, but they were as eager for news as the Germans. Surreptitiously the guards brought the parts for Alfred to assemble. His orders were to hide the set immediately when the music ceased.

Thus on Sunday evening at six, December 17, Alfred turned on the radio while Walter and his group played loudly. The guards had even brought over additional food for supper. Afterward Walter and one of the guards checked with Alfred about the news.

"The German forces are pushing the Allies back," he said. Alfred reported what was to be known in the West as The Battle of the Bulge. It had started the day before at 5:00 A.M. and was sweeping the Allies toward the sea.

The Romanian guard grinned broadly. "Good! The right side is winning."

But it was not to last—neither the German counteroffensive in the West, nor the situation at Caracal. The Russians were already planning their final shipment from the camp. The guards sensed this and began issuing warm Romanian winter wear to the German soldiers. "We want you to be civilians. It will be better this way," they said.

The Germans knew their time was running out, but they were glad for the change of clothing anyway. Their own summer military wear was hardly sufficient for the bitter winds blowing down from the Russian steppes. A fur-lined cap, leather coat with lamb's-wool lining, wool pants, and high-top boots completed the outfit.

The Romanian officer issued the clothing with a friendly smile. "We Romanians would like to keep you Germans right here until the war is over," he said.

The Germans nodded with a hearty, "Ja!"

Toward the end of January the wind brought a new snowfall. Drifts formed along the sides of the barracks, while the gale swept some pockets near the corners clean. Icicles hung like crystal jewels from the ragged tips of the barbed wire. The old camp cemetery was almost buried. Just a few headstones and crosses protruded above the mantle of white. The railroad tracks running parallel with the front gate were no longer visible from the barracks. One would have to go to the entrance to see even the slightest evidence of the presence of rails. Probably this was the reason the sudden appearance of boxcars on the siding came as such a shock to the inmates of Caracal. Without warning, without the slightest noise, they just materialized. The wind had muffled the sound of the train's approach. The Russians had finally arrived.

2

THE Romanian guards quickly distributed supplies of concentrated army rations, enough to last for two weeks if carefully divided. It was the first inkling of the ordeal ahead. In every barrack there was low talk. Anxious men with drawn faces desperately tried to find solace and strength from fellow prisoners, but who could offer help?

"I'll try to stay with you," Walter told Alfred.

This proved impossible. The Reds soon took over the whole camp, and in the confusion of loading prisoners the two friends became separated.

The Russians, without regard for sex, pushed and prodded men and women into line like so many cattle, fifty to

Sunset Over Makeyevka

a boxcar. Inside each car the prisoners found a makeshift double-decker arrangement so that the more agile were forced to jump to a higher platform. The cars knew no bunks, blankets, heat, or toilet facilities—just bare floor and darkness. Once the bolt was slipped into place and the door locked from the outside, the prisoners could see a few narrow streaks of daylight through the siding. Logé felt fortunate to be able to find a spot on the top section near a small crack. While the cars were cold, he knew that before long fresh air would be scarce. He would get the benefit from the body heat below and, by pressing close to the boards, have a little slit for breathing and viewing.

He checked his pockets and cap to see if he had all his possessions. While he had discarded his Red Cross armband because he had no further need of it with civilian clothing, he did retain his collapsible field razor and five old blades. He also had his tin cup fastened to his belt with a piece of twine. His wife had given him a pocket-size edition of the Gospel of Luke, and this he kept securely hidden in his cap. He knew he had more than most prisoners, and he felt grateful.

The Russians had promised to open the doors in about six hours. As he understood most of what the Russians said, Walter relayed what he heard. But he was amazed to find that few in his car understood any German. How, he wondered, had the Reds selected these prisoners of "German descent?"

Many of the poor souls were sobbing, and Walter wanted to communicate some courage. "Keep calm and trust in God," he said so all could hear. But he sensed that his words fell on ears that could not understand.

Perhaps, he thought, it is well that the others could not interpret all the Russians said.

"If a knife is found in any car, ten will die," had been

a Russian guard's last words when he locked the door.

They needed a knife regardless of the threat. Fortunately, one of the prisoners had had the presence of mind to retain his jacknife. He had secreted this on his person and was soon busily engaged in cutting a hole for a toilet. It took him half a day to complete the job, but finally there was some accommodation. Several could not wait for this, and within a few hours the whole interior reeked with the smell of human waste. Obviously they would all be reduced to the level of animals before long. It was hard to conceive of the conditions if they had been without the hole.

Slowly the train made its way through the white Romanian landscape. Often it stopped at sidings and made seemingly endless switches, but generally it progressed eastward.

Two days later the Reds opened the doors. By then the prisoners were nearly mad with thirst. Some could not wait until the guards brought around the water which was supposed to suffice for both food and drink. They leaped into the snow and forced great scoops of it into their mouths. Many were sick and retching. Those who, like Walter, had a tin cup were fortunate. Many still had dried vomit around their lips, but the Russians expected everyone to drink from the same ladle.

The long, monotonous days dragged into a nightmare of unreality. Days dissolved into nights in an endless montage of misery. With aching limbs and bone-chilled bodies the prisoners endured the torture of those cruel hours when they could do nothing but stare blankly into the dimness of the boxcars and see the outlines of fellow sufferers. When they reached the Russian steppes, the wind whistled through the cracks and sent sharp fingers of cold jabbing into the interior. Logé feared he would have a recurrence of his joint malady. He had been in good shape when they loaded, but he felt that only by a slim chance could he expect to endure all the way to Siberia. By alternately stretching and relaxing he exercised as best he could.

"I must not get laid up now," he said to himself. "I've got to keep the circulation going."

The Red guards riding at each end of the train would periodically send a burst of machine gun fire along the sides to frighten the occupants. Sometimes it was for real. Those who were foolish enough to try a break during the water stops were cut down on the spot. Once there was a small slaughter when several stampeded for a watering trough in a peasant's farmyard. Walter always stayed as close to the car as possible. He had no intention of venturing away and tempting the trigger-eager Reds.

A few others, like Walter, tried to warn the prisoners to ration their meager supply of food. Some were so hungry that they had eaten everything within the first few days. Others who knew better simply ate because there was nothing else to do. The Russians began adding cabbage soup to the hot-water menu after the first week. This always felt good going down, but afterward it created such hunger pangs that many sat down in the cars and wept aloud.

The train never seemed to gain much speed. At first the prisoners blamed it on the snow, but even when they reached the vast, wind-swept steppes where the tracks were blown clean, the train still crawled. The rate was always slow, slower, or stop. It was tantalizing to look through the toilet hole and see the ties pass by so slowly. With a little larger hole they could have slipped out even while the train was moving.

After four excruciating weeks they reached the outskirts of Makeyevka, about 12 miles east of Stalino. The sun had just slipped beyond the distant horizon, blushing the scattering clouds with brilliant hues. The prisoners, unloading after their tedious trip, stood for a few seconds taking in the sight. Their eyes, so accustomed to the misery about them, soaked in the twilight scene. In those brief moments they saw that even hell could be beautiful.

Less than a mile away they could see the Makeyevka prison camp with its rows of great stone barracks and small outhouses in the rear. A grim necklace of bare light bulbs was strung above the barbed wire, illuminating the whole enclosure. This was to be the home-not-so-sweet-home for the unwilling visitors from Romania.

For those who could still walk, it felt good to stretch their legs again. For others, half dead from exposure or disease, it meant dragging their tortured bodies along the last mile. For these, the terrible trip was a premature funeral procession. Their burial would take place a few days after arrival.

As Walter Logé marched along toward the barracks, he felt thankful. His legs were still in fairly good shape, he was warm in his Romanian wear, and, best of all, he had not been shipped to Siberia. In fact, he knew most of this area, as he had come this way earlier in the war. "Maybe," he mused, "I can make a break from this place. I shall have to watch and see." It would take some careful scheming, but he was already beginning to lay plans.

The inside of the barracks dripped with dampness, and the moisture penetrated to the marrow. The Russians provided no stoves or blankets, only a little straw on the bunks, and this had long since become soggy. The only other accommodations were the bricks placed at the head of each bunk for a pillow.

That first evening the prisoners were happy to stand in line for their ration of hot water. This was supper. While not nourishing, it would be the only warm thing in their cold lives until the sun came up again.

Walter kept hoping he would find Alfred Mattern somewhere, but the Russians were too restrictive at first. He would have to wait until the camp settled into a routine to make his search.

Three days later the men and women were placed in separate barracks and then sorted for work details. Walter's group was marched off five miles to a coal mine. Fortunately he was assigned to load the coal onto railroad cars. It would be backbreaking work, but at least he would be aboveground. Walter had been idle so long that it actually felt good to be doing something again. Even with his limited strength he began to shovel with a will. The Russian foreman watched him with a big smile, and several times that first day he motioned for Walter to stop and rest.

For those who produced in the work program, the Russians furnished borsch three times a day in addition to the hot water. The prisoners had lost so much weight that their clothes hung like sacks over their frail frames. This soup would not add weight, but it would give some strength to carry on. Those who, like Logé, could work were happy to have anything that resembled food.

A few mornings later Walter had an accident that sent him to the barracks for the sick and crippled. He slipped on the frozen ground in front of the main gate and twisted his right leg violently. There would be no work from him that day or the next, but it would bring him into contact with Alfred again.

He found Alfred, and after the first happy exchange of greetings he looked his friend over carefully. Physically Alfred was not the same man that had left Romania. The ordeal of four weeks, with the lack of food, had contorted his face with pain and hunger.

"Just what are they doing to keep you alive?" Walter asked.

"Not much. A little borsch. If you can't work, they haven't much to spare."

Walter looked about him. The bunks were filled with those too sick or too crippled to work. Some apparently were dying.

Alfred tried to smile. "I'm going to make it. One good thing—the Reds shipped in another group from the West, and now we have a German doctor and a nurse here. They don't have anything to work with, but at least they're in the camp. Sister Gerda brings what little extra she can scrounge from the Red guards."

Walter stood erect and tried to take a few painful steps. "I'll get back on the job in a few days and see if I can bring you something too."

Alfred nodded.

When Walter did return to work, he determined to capitalize on the friendliness of the Russian foreman in the rail yard. It might be the key to escape and might furnish Alfred with a little extra food. He had never spoken to any Russian since his capture, but now he felt the time had come. As the foreman did not live at the camp, Walter felt safe in speaking to him. He did not want any of the women guards who patrolled the fence around the Makeyevka camp to know he understood them, however.

The foreman was all smiles when he saw Logé return for work. It would be much easier to fill the quota of coal now. Walter wanted to wait for the right moment before uncorking his Russian. It must come as a psychological shock. Several hours later, just as Walter expected, the foreman motioned for him to stop and rest.

"You know," said Walter deliberately, "I could do much better if I had more food."

The eyes of the foreman seemed to stand out of their sockets. "So you know the language!"

"Some." Walter sat down and mopped his brow with the back of his hand.

"Where did you learn?"

"Several years ago when we first came into your country. I used to play the balalaika in the evenings for your people."

The Russian understood. Here was a man willing to fraternize. Without hesitation he pointed toward a small whitewashed building about fifty yards away.

"My house is the first one on the right, across the tracks. Tell my wife I sent you."

This was all Walter needed. He was after food, but there was a bit of bargaining he had in mind too. If he was ever to get out of the country he must own Russian clothing.

The foreman's wife was a typical stout Russian woman with a large round face and powerful shoulders. Her shapeless figure filled the doorway. She took one look at Walter and beckoned him in. She seemed to know what the man wanted even before he could tell her. She offered him some of her black bread and a little milk.

It was hard for Walter to show restraint, but between mouthfuls he commented, "I appreciate this so much. You will never know."

The woman nodded. Her eyes scanned Walter from cap to toe, taking in the Romanian cap, coat, pants, and boots. Walter pretended not to notice. He had planned to begin bargaining about clothes, but with solid food before him, everything else could wait. He finished the last of the milk and broke off a little bread to take back to Alfred.

Then he asked, "You like my outfit?"

"Very much."

"Do you have anything to trade for it?" He wanted to

act casual and feared that his voice betrayed his excitement. He hoped she would interpret his speech troubles only as an effort to pronounce the Russian correctly.

She shook her head.

"Can you get something?"

"Only summer wear." Her eyes brightened a little. "Would you take two uniforms for one?"

Walter thought a moment. He didn't want to seem too anxious. If she could get him two light Russian outfits in exchange for what he was wearing it would be better than one. Walter thought he might even dicker for a little cash too.

"I will have to see the clothes first," he said.

The woman smiled. "Tomorrow. You come tomorrow and I will have the clothes for you." She smiled more broadly, showing a row of stubby teeth and a mass of gums. Holding up two fingers, she repeated, "Tomorrow I will have two for one."

Walter thanked her for the food and left feeling satisfied. He was thankful for the extra nourishment, but more about the proposed clothing deal. He knew from the way she had talked that he would strike a bargain.

The next day the foreman sent Walter directly to his house for the trade. He seemed as anxious as his wife for the transaction. Undoubtedly they both thought this German simply didn't know the value of good clothing. They have no idea what's brewing, thought Walter Logé.

The foreman's wife had the clothes spread out on the hearth when Walter walked in. There was the blue mechanic's uniform and cap, and a green army uniform without a cap. Walter felt the weight of them, then unbuttoned his own coat to show its thickness.

"How many rubles will you put with the two uniforms?"

Without a word the woman went to a shelf and picked

up a box containing a little money. She held up two rubles. Walter shook his head. Five. He still refused. He didn't want to press the issue too far, but he sensed she was willing to continue. Finally they reached that point where good bargaining ceases. Two Russian summer outfits and fifteen rubles for one Romanian winter set, and it was a deal.

The woman turned her back while Walter changed in the corner of the one-room house. He used the green clothes for underwear, and into the right-hand pocket he slipped the razor, blades, and rubles. The Gospel of Luke he transferred to the inside of the blue cap. He ran his belt through the tin cup handle on the outside.

When he had made the change, he walked toward the door. "How do I look?" he smiled.

She laughed outright. "Go show my husband!"

Walter returned to work, and the foreman greeted him pleasantly. "Now you are one of us."

It was just what Walter wanted to hear. "I want to look like you, talk like you, and work like you," he said, feeling pleased with his double meaning, which he felt sure the foreman did not discern.

That evening when Walter returned from work it was too dark in the barracks to show Alfred his new acquisitions. "Wait until morning. You'll laugh at the change," Walter whispered hoarsely. "I really look like one of them now."

"I'm puzzled," said Alfred. "Just how can you keep suspicion down in this camp?"

"They'll never know. There are too many of us, and with that last shipment I notice a lot of Russian castoffs being worn. The Reds have shipped so many in here that you can see almost every kind of uniform now. These women guards rotate shifts, and they can't possibly keep

3—S.E.

track of each prisoner's looks. They only do a morning and evening head count."

Walter started to leave for his own barracks; then he came back and whispered in Alfred's ear.

"I got fifteen rubles in the trade too. Not bad for a slave, eh?"

Alfred snickered. "I'm glad for you."

With the German doctor and Sister Gerda around, Walter felt the time had come to plan his escape. Whatever could be done for the sick and wounded, they would be available. His conscience was clear about that matter; Alfred Mattern would be in good hands. At Caracal he had remained, but now he determined to make a break for it. He had no specific plans at the moment; but he knew that if he watched and waited the right combination would come.

A few nights later, en route to the outhouse, Logé noticed the women guards huddled together outside the fence. They paid little heed to Walter, but continued their jabbering. Ordinarily he never bothered to listen to them, but this night something caught his attention. Inside the privy he listened carefully, to pick up every word.

"If another light bulb blows there's no replacement," one of the guards said.

"That's good to know," Walter smiled to himself.

Many times he had observed the slight depression under the fence near his barracks. There was just enough room for a man to wiggle under if he had time. The guards' skill with their machine guns was proverbial, and he had always dropped the idea before. But now a plan suggested itself.

The bare light bulbs, strung unevenly above the high barbed wire, glared down in the prison yard. Their light made the scattered snow glisten, adding a starkness to the shadow effect of posts, wire, and barracks.

Logé walked directly from the privy to the barracks, but instead of entering he slipped into the shadows. Kicking a clod of frozen earth loose, he picked it up in his hands and listened. He heard the groans and murmuring of the prisoners within and the raucous talking of the guards without. In the shadows he was safe from being seen, but was he far enough away not to be heard? This could be a big step in his plans if he could get away with it. He could feel his heart begin to race. Looking about him to make sure no one was watching, he took careful aim at his target about thirty feet away and threw the clod in his hand as hard as he could. The light bulb over the depression shattered. The noise startled him more than he thought it would. He braced himself against the wall, expecting the guards to come running. He waited and listened, ready to dash around the opposite side of the barracks should they appear. He felt safer now in the gathering darkness, but with his thinner clothing and the tension of the situation, he shivered violently.

Walter waited at least fifteen minutes before he could muster up enough courage to peer around the corner. When he did, the guards were beginning to patrol the fence again.

One of those who had advanced farther toward Walter called back to the others, "I see another one has burned out!"

With this Walter slipped inside and went to his bunk. In spite of the goose pimples, he felt a sensation of inner warmth. His days at Makeyevka, he hoped, were numbered.

The next day during his morning break Walter pressed the foreman for one last request.

"I have a needy friend back in camp. Would it be possible for me to buy a little extra food at the bazaar?"

The foreman looked at Walter and then toward the marketplace a quarter of a mile away. His eyes narrowed as he thought about the whole procedure. It was one thing to allow a prisoner to do some trading in his home nearby, and another to let him leave the work area completely. Walter sensed the struggle going on in the foreman's mind.

"I will be back in fifteen minutes. You can trust me."

It was not a matter of trusting him. The foreman knew if he gave an alarm his prisoner would be rounded up in a short while, but he did not want any of the prison authorities to know he granted this kind of permission. He looked directly into Walter Logé's eyes.

"Buy what you want, but talk as little as possible."

Walter understood. He thanked the guard and was off toward the market. This was good advice to remember for the future. Obviously his German accent gave him away.

Later, when he returned to work, he carried with him two cans with American labels, one of meat, the other of beans. He also had a loaf of Russian black bread, a bottle of milk, and two eggs.

"And I never had to say more than a few words," he told the foreman.

Walter saw relief written all over the foreman's face. He laughed heartily. He seemed to like this prisoner. Walter could tell from the way he chatted the rest of the day that many more privileges would come his way if he needed them. But Walter hoped he wouldn't be around to use them.

That evening Walter gave Alfred the two eggs, the milk, and part of the bread.

"It is a good thing to pay tithe," he explained. "I want to leave this with you just like a tithe. It will be a blessing to both of us."

Alfred looked puzzled. "Tithe?"

Walter tried to explain, but Alfred obviously could not grasp his religious ideas, and he changed the subject. "I am leaving tonight. I will get word to your wife in Berlin when I arrive."

Tears welled up in Alfred's eyes. He gripped Walter's hands and held them tightly. Finally he spoke. "Your legs? Will they hold out?"

"They haven't given me trouble since Caracal."

"It's a long way to Berlin."

Walter did not comment. The two sat in silence for a few minutes, then they shook hands. Perhaps this would be the last time.

"I want to leave right after the head count tonight," Walter whispered.

Perhaps it was the excitement of the venture, overwork in the coal yard, or a combination of both, but he could not leave that night. Suddenly feeling ill, he spent a restless night and part of the next day in his bunk.

In the meantime Alfred had spread the word to several others of Walter's intentions. One by one six men came to Walter with whispered pleas to escape with him. Walter knew Alfred had meant well, but he was shocked to realize so many knew of his plans.

To each Logé gave the same reply. "You don't know the language, and without Russian clothing it will be nearly impossible."

All six agreed it would be risky, but they wanted to follow him out of Makeyevka anyway. Although he desperately tried to discourage them, he finally agreed to take them.

"You must do exactly as I tell you. Follow one by one at about ten-minute intervals. Be sure the women are not patrolling. They usually are together at the far end. I will signal by a bird call in the willows on the way to the sauna bath."

They understood. Once every week the Russians marched the prisoners a mile to a sauna bath and delousing ovens for their clothing. The clump of willows stood in a little hollow about halfway.

The evening they were to leave, all seven watched the sunset with keen interest. It was not spectacular, but it was meaningful. Somewhere out there where the huge ball rested on the horizon was home. In a little while there would be a final head count and then darkness. Just a matter of hours now.

3

EXCEPT for a slight spring breeze the night air was still. For the past few days the weather had warmed until a general thawing was felt throughout the vast plains. In the distance frogs croaked from a thousand ponds and puddles. The guards tramped their perfunctory rounds along the muddy path outside the fence.

The moment came just as the women gathered in their usual cluster to talk. Without the slightest hesitation Walter slipped into the darkness by the depression and wriggled under the fence. The mud felt soft and cool to his hands. He knew there would be telltale tracks, but by morning he and the other six should be many miles away.

Escape Toward the Setting Sun

One by one the men were guided to the willow clump by Walter's low whistles. When the last man joined the group, they all felt such a sense of freedom that they barely resisted shouting and singing. The relief was like an electric shock. They dared not make a sound, but silently they shook hands all around as only men who have just escaped the clutches of a slave camp can.

Within Walter's heart swelled thankfulness to a kind Providence who had led him thus far. He would need much more for the trip ahead. Silently he prayed for guidance. It was such a long way from Makeyevka to Berlin.

Once the initial thrill had subsided Logé led the men into the night. Quietly they marched along single file, just keeping each other in sight. After several hours they came to a small ditch and Walter motioned for the men to rest. "We'd better take on a little nourishment now."

He had personally saved enough rations for about three days, and he knew the others had been able to get some roasted sunflower seeds. But before long all would have to begin begging food from peasants. This would mean extra hazards, the kind he dreaded from the first.

The men ate in silence, each wrapped up in his own thoughts. Walter wanted to think of home, but the problem of the other men kept crowding this out. He had promised to lead them away from the prison camp, but how far did that mean? He had told them he would set the pace and any that felt like dropping behind would be free to do so. He knew from the start that if he were ever to make it to Berlin it would have to be alone. They knew it too, but somehow they all wanted to stay with him as long as they could. The difficulties of staying together would be compounded once the alarm was given. Walter became restless just thinking about it, and shortly motioned for the men to resume walking.

Imperceptibly the faint gray light of early dawn began to creep over the land. They were now trudging on the outskirts of the great Stalino airfield. Walter recognized it from the star pattern of the runways. They would have to find a hiding place quickly, as sentries would be on duty here. And then it happened.

Off to one side a lone sentry was coming directly toward them. There was no time to hide, no chance to change directions.

Walter did not wait to be challenged. "Dobriy vecher!" he shouted loudly.

"Dobroye utro!" the sentry called back.

Instantly Logé knew his own greeting was a mistake. He should have used the morning salutation, not "good evening." It would be only a matter of time now. Silently they walked along the periphery of the airfield without looking back.

About two miles farther on they came to a huge ammunition dump with rows and rows of bombs placed pyramid fashion as high as a house. To the side of these were stacks of discarded Stuka bomb tubes which had been left by the retreating Germans.

"Quickly!" ordered Walter. "Each man get into a tube. Don't move— Not a sound. Don't cough, sneeze, or whisper. I will tell you when it is safe to come out. That sentry has probably phoned about us already."

The men scrambled into the empty casings. Walter backed into one near a bomb pyramid, adjusting the dead weeds and grass so he could peer out. They had acted just in time.

Within minutes it seemed the whole Stalino command was alive. Two planes circled overhead. In the distance the fugitives could hear an infantry officer counting cadence. At first they were tense. Their hearts beat rapidly and seemed to resound inside their hollow hideouts, announcing their whereabouts. As time passed, however, they relaxed enough to sleep fitfully. Thirst was their main problem. As the long day wore on, their lips cracked and their mouths seemed stuffed with cotton.

From his position Walter could see the weeds in front of his casing casting strange shadow patterns. The deep shade by the pyramids indicated that the men would be able to leave their cramped quarters soon. He wanted to resume walking right after sundown.

At last, when the sky began to take on an orange hue, Walter felt he must peer out. Parting the weeds for a better view, he saw a Russian officer, standing atop the nearest pyramid, slowly sweeping the horizon with his binoculars. Carefully Walter eased himself farther back into the tube. What if one of the men, weary with waiting, should happen to make a noise?

When it was darker, Walter peered out again. The officer was gone. The moon was not up, but enough light shone from the city for him to see easily. He was glad the Russians saw no more need of a blackout.

"Get up, get up," he whispered hoarsely.

The men must have been ready, because each came out of hiding in a hurry. Clustered around Walter, they bent and stretched to regain their circulation.

"We'll move away from here before eating," Walter said. "It will be good to walk for a while."

The whole region was permeated with the odor of rotting cabbage, but after a mile the scent became so strong that the men knew they were nearing a storage stack. Following their noses, they discovered the straw heap which protected the cabbage. Digging through this they uncovered large solid heads. Tearing off the blackened outer leaves, they began satisfying their voracious appetites.

They thought they could eat several heads of the moist cabbage, but they soon found that one head apiece was sufficient. Biting off chunks, they ate greedily until they began to realize they were eating much too rapidly for their own good.

Shortly after they began walking again, one man complained of stomach cramps and dropped behind. Others followed. Somewhere during the night Walter Logé lost all six of them. Except for a few brief periods of rest, he walked on, never slackening his steady pace. The long rest in the Stuka tube had made him feel like hiking all night.

"If my legs will hold out and I don't get sick, I think I can do this every night," he said to himself.

He planned to get his bearings each evening from the westerly sun and walk at night. As the season progressed more toward the summer, the sun would be setting farther to the north, which would make it about right for Berlin according to his calculations. He determined not to let time and distance discourage him. He mustn't think of the possibility of failure. He must get home!

Light began to filter through the eastern sky when Walter came to a large strawstack. It was far removed from any farmhouse or village, but, even though it was still only predawn, Walter stopped.

"I'd better not press my luck," he said. "This will be just the thing until night comes again."

Wiggling feetfirst into the end of the stack, he used his hands to cover the opening with loose straw. The straw felt soft and warm, and he adjusted himself for a long sleep. In a few moments, however, he realized he had company. Mice had discovered his warm body and were scampering up his trouser legs, down his sleeves, and through the neck opening. Their cold noses tickled, and he chuckled audibly.

"Go to sleep, little ones, and don't give me your kisses," Walter whispered.

In spite of the visitors Walter soon fell asleep. The sun was fully up when he suddenly awakened to the sound of voices. A group of peasants had come with pitchforks to take away a load of straw. When he heard their forks jamming into the stack it startled him so that he had to peek. Carefully parting the straw, he peered out. Nothing. Easing himself out a little, he pulled the straw loose from the corner so he could look around. The peasants were working the other end. Walter ducked back and smiled as he rearranged the straw again. All was well. He was sure they would never use the whole stack in a day.

Three hours later another group came for straw. This time Logé heard them, but he did not bother to watch. He felt quite safe. He was warm and cozy, and the mice had settled down since he first came into their domain. He slept soundly at times, and at others drifted in a twilight zone of semislumber. During these periods he usually managed to return to Berlin as his thoughts and dreams carried him back to his loved ones.

Besides wanting to be with his family, he had promised to tell Alfred Mattern's wife of her husband's whereabouts.

During his reveries one scene was especially vivid. On the night of January 12, 1944, when he was about to leave again for the front after a three-week furlough, his children had tugged on his arms trying to prevent him from reaching the door.

"You can't leave us!" they had cried.

Walter had looked toward his dear, plucky wife, Irma, and their eyes had met in sympathetic understanding.

He could hear her telling the children not to beg. "You will have to let Daddy go now, or the Gestapo will be after him."

The final parting at the door with the children still cling-
ing to him had been so impressive that their uncle Holdi
had painted a picture of it. In Walter's mind he could even
see that picture, which was hanging on the wall the last
time he had been home.

How were the children? Walter saw them one by one.
Little Doris would be five in May. Ursel would be nine in
June. His boy, Dieter, would turn seven in July. Poor Ursel
had been so nervous and upset over the incessant bombings
that Irma had sent her to relatives in the Riesen Gebirge
region of Sudetenland. Doris and Dieter were always different. So gay and always happy—too gay at times. Walter
could see them dancing around him, laughing and singing.
His mind picked up the scene and followed it for a while.

A little over a month after that furlough he had been
wounded in action and sent to a military hospital in Landau on the Isar River in Bavaria. Here, during his convales-
cence, he had a surprise visit from his wife and two youn-
gest children on April 23, his birthday. He had been
sleeping face up in the hospital garden when Doris and
Dieter had placed a birthday cake with a lighted candle
right on his stomach. Walter felt himself smile involuntarily as he thought of it. The two had danced and clapped
their hands, teasing him about their little trick.

When he finally awoke in the haystack, it was late afternoon. He would have to wait a few more hours before
walking again. Nibbling on his dried bread, he wondered
just how far he could go without stopping to beg for food.

That evening Logé followed the wagon tracks west. The
weather was getting warmer, and both horse-drawn and
motor vehicles left ruts in the muddy road. On and on he
trudged into the night, stopping only a few times for rest.
It was a slow, steady pace, but it ate up the miles. Somewhere in the night he finished the last of his rations. After

that he knew no matter how often he stopped for rest it would not supply him with energy to keep going.

"I'll have to get food when morning comes," he said to himself. "I've got to have something for these legs to go on."

With the first tinge of morning light, Walter began seeking a lonely farmhouse off the main road. He knew it would be relatively safe to ask for food at such a place because most of these farms had no electricity or telephone. Most of the menfolk were away to war. Those that remained here usually worked near the villages as farm foremen or supervisors. From the start he knew the source of his food supply would be the generous Russian peasants. They would not turn away a hungry stranger.

A mile off to his right Walter finally spotted a farmhouse and barn standing starkly against the vast sweep of the horizon. The sun had cast its dawn hues along the whitewashed sides and colored them a warm pink. The house looked inviting.

It was a typical peasant dwelling made of sun-dried cow manure and straw bricks, plastered within and without. In sharp contrast to the whitewashed sides was the thatched roof that had blackened with age. Walter had visited so many peasants during the days when his unit first plunged into Russia that he knew exactly what he would find within—only one room with a large fireplace and oven combination, with a sleeping loft above.

When Walter knocked at the door, a barefooted woman faced him. Her stout frame nearly filled the doorway. Two sleepy-eyed children, a little boy and a little girl, peered around the sides of her skirt. Standing there in the morning sun, she listened while Walter explained why he needed food. Without a word she nodded and motioned for him to enter. It was as simple as that.

The fearlessness of the Russian peasant women was proverbial. Even with their husbands away they never feared to let a stranger enter their homes.

"They are so well built that they needn't be afraid of any man," Walter had often commented.

The woman motioned Walter toward a chair. "Sit down, and I'll get you something to eat."

The children clung to her skirt like a pair of leeches. Walter winked at them, but they only ducked out of sight behind their mother.

The woman poured a glass of milk from a pitcher and set a loaf of black bread and some cold boiled potatoes before Walter. After several gulps he wiped his mouth with the back of his sleeve and broke off a chunk of the bread.

"Everything tastes so good," he smiled.

The woman pulled up a chair across from Logé and sat down. The children stood behind her, their faces barely visible to Walter.

"You say you have escaped from prison," she spoke softly, her voice barely audible. "What kind of prison?"

Walter did not want to mention the exact prison for fear she might report it later on and the authorities could trace his route, but he did want to convey what was happening in her country.

"A concentration camp with all kinds of prisoners—even some Russians, probably political prisoners."

She leaned forward slightly and fastened her eyes on Walter.

"Is that true?"

"True. I was there. I saw it. There were Germans, Romanians, Russians, all kinds, many nationalities. It was awful. You become only a number there." He paused and took another bite of bread. "And they work without much food—men and women as slaves."

"Where have you been staying?"

Walter laughed, and almost choked, for his mouth was full. "I had a soft bed for my last sleep. I shared a straw-stack with some mice."

At this the children giggled. They had grown bolder and stood by the table now, their eyes peering over the edge. Walter laughed again and waved at them. The woman beamed at her youngsters, nodding her approval.

"Eat all you want. You must be very hungry."

Walter told her about his own family and his home in Berlin. He talked about the war and how good it would be to have it over. News traveled only by word of mouth in her area, but she told him that it sounded as if Germany was about to fall.

For a few minutes there was silence as each seemed shut in by the private thoughts about the war itself, the horrors, the separations, and how good it would be to have peace again. Finally the woman broke the stillness of the little room.

"You will stay here for a while, won't you?" She swept her hand in a gesture that conveyed spaciousness despite the contrary evidence. "We have room. There's just the two children and myself. You can sleep right on the floor by the hearth."

Her words sounded good to Walter. He could shave, get some rest, and devour more food before moving on.

4

WALTER LOGE left the peasant home the next morning. The woman gave him a loaf of bread and pointed the way. As he waved good-bye to her and the children he realized this would be his first time on the road in daylight. It would have its hazards, he knew.

The first of these came when he tried to get a drink of water from a village well. Uncoiling the string he had brought, he tied it to the tin can he used for a cup and lowered it into the well. Try as he would, it would only float on the surface. For a long time he toyed with the can as it teasingly bobbed around. He knew he should devise some other method, but his mind would not function

Dnepropetrovsk --
Round Trip

along inventive lines right then. Finally he was able to get about a tablespoon of water, but fearing others might come to the well, he moved on.

"I'll just have to wait until dark and get my water from some farm," he decided.

Whether it was caused by drinking from the same source the farm animals used or by the food he had eaten, Walter never knew, but within the next twenty-four hours he was stricken with diarrhea.

With stomach cramps and nausea he fought to keep on his feet. Hours wore into days—nights and days, on and on. Time became meaningless. There were more strawstacks, more farmhouses—old barns and mangers—sleeping in ditches—drinking from watering troughs and wells—he staggered and fought to keep going. He prayed as he stumbled on.

"Oh, God, give me strength. Berlin is so far!"

In spite of his illness he finally reached a hamlet not far from the Dnieper River. Hungry and exhausted, he made his way to the first house. It was a neat, two-room frame building set apart from the rest on the edge of the town. It looked inviting, but he knew it would be risky to knock. While he was about over his sickness, he needed good food and a place to rest before trying to find a way across the Dnieper. He must make the gamble.

An elderly man answered the door. He was slightly stooped and had a shock of gray hair just over his forehead. Except for his searching eyes he bore an almost benign, fatherly look.

Walter smiled weakly and greeted him in the very best Russian he could.

"I've escaped from a prison in the east and need food and rest," he said bluntly.

His accent, the gaunt look, and soiled clothing seemed

to be evidence enough. The man scrutinized Walter's face.

"What's your name?"

"Logé, Walter Logé."

He knew the man was wondering about his French name, but right then Walter did not feel like explaining his Huguenot background.

The man opened the door wide and motioned with his hand to Walter. "Step in here." He offered Walter the chair behind his own desk and then stood with his back to the door. "Just why have you escaped?"

"It was awful. They work you too hard for the amount of food and you have to sleep in a wet barracks with no blankets. You are only a number."

"I know. I hear things like this all the time."

The man looked away from Walter. His eyes were not focused on anything in particular in the room, but he seemed to be gazing off into the distance. After a few moments he faced Walter again.

"You will stay here tonight and tomorrow we shall go to Dnepropetrovsk."

Walter's eyes widened. "What? To Dnepropetrovsk?" Then he smiled. "That is exactly where I want to go. I never could swim, and I have been wondering how I could cross the big river."

For the first time Walter sensed there was something strange about the man. His smile, though very slight, did not match the touch of irony in his voice.

"You shall go to Dnepropetrovsk all right—first class."

While Walter had unwittingly walked into the home of the local Communist deputy (mayor), he was being treated with respect and care. Perhaps it was Walter's complete honesty and frankness, but at any rate the deputy furnished him with a warm supper that evening.

From the window Walter watched a guard leading six

Russians to a privy. It was located just behind a brick house next door. When they were returned, the guard locked the door. Walter could see the prisoners peering through the bars on the windows, and he wondered if he would be joining them for the evening. Instead, the deputy furnished a bed right in his own office, and Walter spent one of the best nights he had had for a long time.

The next morning an armed guard appeared at the door to escort Walter to the train station. The deputy followed several paces behind, but when they boarded the train he ordered several passengers to move from seats so he and Walter could sit together. Even the guard remained standing in the rear of the car. "Sit by the window," the deputy said; "I want you to see the great river."

Walter smiled. "Thank you."

As the train moved out over the railroad bridge, Walter's heart swelled with thankfulness. Whatever the future held he knew God would take care of him. Now he was happy for the pleasure of a free ride across a barrier that had secretly haunted him ever since he had escaped from Make-yevka.

"Quite a river to have to swim," chuckled the deputy.

Walter did not turn his face away from the window. "Yes," he replied, "it must be at least a kilometer wide."

"Just how do you think you could have made it across if I did not take you?"

Again Walter thought he detected that note of sarcasm. For a moment their eyes met.

"I don't know. I do not worry about the future."

Walter looked out the window again. He really did not want to talk just then. He simply wanted to enjoy every moment of the free ride toward the west and to continue silently giving thanks.

The deputy seemed to sense that Logé was not interested in conversation; so he remained silent himself. When the train pulled into the Dnepropetrovsk station, he quietly signaled to the guard to take Walter away. "I am turning you over to the authorities here," he said as he arose. "I trust you will find better quarters than at the place from which you escaped."

The old man started to leave; then he turned and faced Walter and looked deeply into his eyes. "I have appreciated your candor." With this remark he walked away.

Here was a man who seemed to be torn by an inner conflict. On one hand he felt obligated to carry out the duties assigned him by higher authorities, and yet he appeared to be sympathetic with this strange escapee.

"Thank you for the ride," said Walter, but the deputy was lost in the crowd.

Walter was taken to an old factory that had been converted into prison quarters. Rows of empty bunks, three tiers deep, filled the place. There were no blankets, pillows, mattresses, or straw. Except for the lack of dampness it had all the shades of Makeyevka, with the same bleakness.

After passing through the quarters Walter was led away for a physical examination. The woman doctor made a superficial check and then pronounced him fit for work detail. He was immediately assigned the task of cleaning bricks from the massive rubble heaps left by the bombings.

Silently he worked the rest of the day without speaking to anyone or being spoken to. People of many nationalities were incarcerated at Dnepropetrovsk, but toward evening when they lined up for soup, Walter heard someone mumble in German.

Logé walked over to the man and extended his hand. "My name's Walter."

The man looked at him through tired, gray eyes and

extended a limp hand. "Karl," was the prisoner's only reply.

That evening Walter took a bunk just below Karl's and went to sleep quickly. The next thing he knew the Russians were calling for the prisoners to awaken. Walter's cap had tipped back when he slept, and as he reached to put it on he instinctively felt for the Gospel of Luke. It was gone. He looked under his bunk and all around, but the missing pocket edition was not to be found. Paper was so scarce that it sold for five rubles a sheet on the black market. Somehow the prisoners always seemed able to pilfer a little tobacco, and if paper could be had, they would smoke.

Later that day Walter found Karl at the far end of a brick pile away from the guards, and at his feet was a scrap of burned paper. Walter stooped over and picked it up. Nothing was visible except the corner which read, "Luke 24."

"You should never use the Bible this way." Walter scolded him. "You have burned it for nothing. Read it, don't smoke it!"

Karl seemed not to hear. His stooped shoulders and stolid demeanor indicated that he had given up hope long since and cherished every bit of fleeting pleasure that might remain. Life was ebbing away in endless slavery, and he had slipped into a state of dejection from which there was no return. Logé would later feel a tinge of conscience over his manner toward this poor wretch, but at the moment he was upset over the loss of his Scripture portion. It had been such a comfort to him in the past, and now he would be deprived of it simply because some prisoner wanted a smoke. Besides, he himself hated tobacco.

Two mornings later, when the prisoners were awakened for work, Walter noticed there was no response from Karl. He shook him. "Wake up, Karl!" he called.

Walter rolled the man over. One look at that ashen face and a touch of those cold hands was enough. When the guard came over to see why there was a delay, Walter motioned toward Karl. "He's dead."

Prisoners commonly died in their sleep, but somehow Walter could not shake the thought of Karl. The sad, hopeless face kept reappearing in his mind. "If only I had said something to him for encouragement, something to help him along the way, something to give him hope and a little faith," he thought.

He pondered anew the situation at Dnepropetrovsk—the misery and degradation, the endless round of labor. He would have to get on with the business of escape.

The only way to secure favors from the Russians was to work hard. For several days Walter did more than his share of cleaning bricks; and then, just as he thought, he was singled out by a Russian officer. He seemed to know that Walter understood Russian.

"I like the way you work," he said. "I want you to help on a special detail."

The officer smiled in an artificial manner, showing a row of light bluish-gray teeth. Walter had never seen such a mouthful of metal in his life. Many people in Europe had chrome-cobalt alloy teeth, but this man's seemed different. Maybe it was because he displayed them so conspicuously.

Walter stared as the man spoke, and the officer genuinely smiled this time. "You like my dentures? They're made of platinum!"

He seemed to be saying, "My mouth is filled with expensive material, and let everyone, countryman and prisoner alike, know that I have arrived at a status few in Russia possess."

This officer selected Walter and two other German prisoners to ride with him on a train southward, ostensibly to unload an electric motor. The day they left it rained a steady drizzle. The men huddled in the boxcar and watched the drab scenery pass by under a leaden sky. Despite the depressing weather Walter was in a cheerful mood. A premonition about this departure from Dnepropetrovsk seemed to buoy his spirits. He sensed that he would make an escape again. He might be going south, but he was still on the west side of the Dneiper, and by keeping a watchful eye he might soon be under way again.

In the late afternoon they arrived at their destination. After unloading the motor on the station platform the prisoners were ordered to walk to the Russian officer's house on the outskirts of town. The rain had let up some, but they were all wet enough to feel miserable by the time they reached the house. Stepping inside to the warmth of a cheery fire proved a pleasant relief.

"You are fortunate to be able to work for me," the officer smiled, again showing his wondrous dentures. "I will give you good food and a warm place to sleep. Tomorrow you will work for me in the cabbage fields."

"So this is why he brought us down here!" thought Walter.

The other two, not understanding, just stood before the hearth rubbing their hands. Walter translated the remarks into German, and then all three smiled their thankfulness.

True to his word, the officer had his wife prepare a good supper for the prisoners. It seemed the best-tasting black bread and borsch they had eaten in a long time, and they ate till they were full. Walter wished he could save some of the food for later use.

"You can stay in the attic," the officer offered after the meal. Then he laughed coarsely. "It's plenty dry up there."

The attic was dark, but certainly warmer and more comfortable than the old factory at Dnepropetrovsk. Walter lay there listening to the rain on the roof, trying to imagine what the morrow would bring. It was cozy, and he felt very comfortable after eating.

"This man is an odd one," he mused. "I will watch carefully. One mistake on his part is all I will need. Just one mistake, that's all. The field work sounds good."

The next day dawned bright with the prospect. The warm spring sun quickly dispelled the mist hanging low over the swales and ditches. Birds winged swiftly about in their annual business of nesting. A soft breeze swept the vast fields of young cabbage. The ground, still soft from the rain, made it easy to work.

With his characteristic smile the officer handed each prisoner a hoe and pointed to the rows of plants. "Tell the men to be careful for the new shoots." With this he turned and walked back to the house.

Walter smiled inwardly. "He has already made his mistake."

The land extended on all sides like a massive tabletop. In the dim distance could be seen low, undulating hills which gently faded into the horizon. Obviously the officer thought he could keep an eye on the men. Who would try to escape from such a place, with two legs the only transportation?

"I'm going just as soon as there's enough distance between me and the house," Walter said half aloud.

He worked steadily along his row until he had moved several hundred yards away. The solid breakfast gave him the kind of energy he needed, but he had no intention of wasting all of it on hoeing cabbages. He would have to be careful though. The officer might have his field glasses trained on him that very moment. Everything must look normal.

When he was ready, he straightened up to rest and take

the kinks out of his back. He noticed one of the other prisoners within talking distance.

"I'm leaving," Walter said hoarsely. "Do you want to come along?"

The man stopped in his tracks and for a few moments did not answer. The thought had startled him, and he needed time for his mind to engage the proper gears. Looking at Walter, he shook his head slowly. "It would be crazy. The officer can see us from his house, and besides, this country is so flat that it would be impossible." He started to hoe again, but continued talking. "Anyway, just where do you think you'll go?"

Walter dropped his hoe and strode toward the nearest ditch. "Berlin," he said without looking back.

When he reached the ditch he took time to relieve himself. Then, crouching low, he ran. Periodically he stopped to catch his wind and then scurried on. Never mind the direction right then.

"If only I can make it to a strawstack, I'll be safe for a while," he panted.

Before he had run very far he knelt in the mud and prayed. He did not ask for a miracle—only the strength and courage to go on.

For three days Logé made his way across fields, sleeping in strawstacks and avoiding all contacts with people except at the most remote farmhouses. He was back on a dangerous daylight schedule again, but traveling was easier. He could find railroad tracks and follow these, and when the roads were cleared he walked right along, often to the outskirts of the villages. On the third day his luck ran out. A local Communist deputy stopped and interrogated him. Walter's accent and unshaven face caused immediate suspicion.

"Where do you come from?"

"The east," Walter answered warily.

"I know you have escaped from somewhere. I can tell." The man's eyes narrowed to little slits. "Now tell me, why did you leave?"

Walter took a deep breath and straightened himself. "Because I couldn't stand to see people die or be treated like animals."

The deputy wasn't about to hear any more of this. Grabbing Walter by the arm, he shouted, "Come with me!"

The deputy led his captive to his own house and, once inside, locked the door. "Give me your belt," he demanded. "You won't run very far holding up your pants."

Walter handed over his belt. For the first time since leaving Makeyevka he noticed how much weight he had lost. His trousers hung so loosely that it was an effort to keep them from slipping to the floor.

The deputy set Walter near the phone and watched carefully while he called. "We shall see just where you came from," he sneered.

After several attempts the deputy finally contacted the officer who had taken Walter to work in his cabbage field. Walter could only hear what was said at one end of the line, but it was enough.

"Yes, yes. He is in my custody now. Do you want him back?" The deputy glanced at Walter as he spoke. "Yes!" he smiled sarcastically. "Yes, I am sure he will find it much harder. I will see that he gets there."

The Russian put the receiver down and turned to Walter. "Have you ever been to Dnepropetrovsk?"

Walter nodded slowly.

5

THE spring of 1945 brought new worries to Berliners. All Germany was caught in the great, crushing vise of the Allies, but for those in Berlin the news from the east was the most distressing. The Russians were pounding at the city gates. Deep within his bunker under the reichschancellery garden Hitler was ordering the last defenders of the city to take their posts. Young lads of the Hitler Youth, barely able to shoulder a gun, were pressed into service against the advancing Russians. They would have to stand by their posts to the bitter end. But it was not those facing death as soldiers for the Führer who needed to worry so much. Sweeping before the terrible assault was the ava-

Into the Storm

lanche of rumors, reports of Red atrocities and horrors. There was not a woman in Berlin, old or young, who did not have this fear etched into her very soul. The Reds were coming!

Walter Logé could only surmise what might be happening in Berlin, but he knew the results should the Russians enter that city. He often thought about his wife and prayed for her.

* * *

When Walter was brought back to Dnepropetrovsk, he was placed in an old garage with five other prisoners and temporarily relieved of his belt. There were no bunks, but no work was assigned either. He slept on the floor, happy for the chance to conserve his strength.

Several days later he was taken out and briefly interrogated by an officer. On such occasions Walter always stated his name clearly because he sensed the Russians were more lenient with him after they heard his French name. He also was careful never to mention exact places. He honestly could not remember many towns and villages he had passed through, but such a place as Makeyevka created no desire for a return engagement.

The officer sent Walter to the camp doctor for a medical examination. She pronounced him fit for work, and within minutes he was assigned a detail with twenty-four others unloading drill presses and other machinery at the railroad station near the Dnieper River.

Here the prisoners carried on systematic sabotage right under the guard's nose. Whenever his back was turned the workers tossed a few nuts and bolts and removable parts into the murky waters of the river. There was so much noise and confusion at the station anyway that this activity was never detected.

Walter's mind, ever on the alert for an escape, responded to this atmosphere quickly. He spied an old rusty piece of chain about two feet in length, and from then on he was ready to spring. The moment came when several prisoners were trying to lift a heavy piece of machinery off the flatcar. The guard stepped over to give instructions, and Walter grabbed the chain and slipped around the corner of the building and to a lone siding. Following the track as if he were a worker on the railroad, he walked casually away, hoping the chain on his shoulder would add the right atmosphere. It didn't. He had barely gone one kilometer when a railroad inspector saw him and shouted.

"You, with the chain! Halt!"

Walter tried to act nonchalant, but his heart was pounding. Right then he knew his prop was a mistake. "Never again," he muttered to himself.

"Let me see your papers," the inspector ordered.

"I have none."

"None?"

"None."

The inspector's eyes narrowed. "You are just a roughneck—a lawbreaker. Drop that chain!"

Walter let the chain slip from his shoulder.

Once the possible weapon was dropped, the inspector grabbed Walter's arm. "Now come with me."

Back at the camp headquarters, fortunately for Walter, the officer who had interrogated him that morning was not there at the moment. Another camp official handed Walter a little mallet and, without realizing his past, led him back to the old brick-cleaning job. It was much lighter work than the lifting, and there were far more prisoners per guard. Walter felt very happy. He had not been punished for his escape attempt and was suddenly in a position for a better try.

He knew, however, that he would need more food if he wanted to make a break from the city. There would be no more premature rushes now. He would not yield to every opportunity. From then on he begged at the guard's mess hall whenever he could. His face became so familiar at the kitchen door that the cooks began saving scraps and any leftovers they could for him.

Another source of food came from the Russian women. During the daytime, when returning from the open bazaar, they often stood with tears in their eyes watching the prisoners work. In spite of the curses and scolding of the guard, the women would take pity on the men and toss loaves of bread toward them.

"Get away, women!" the guard would shout. "Back to work, you swine!"

The prisoners were deaf. Bread in the streets! Bread! Something more than the two watery meals a day—bread! They were beyond hearing threats, names, vituperation. Rushing, tearing, kicking, clawing, they fought for every scrap like wild dogs. Walter and a few others were wise enough to wait until the scramble was on and then catch some of the loaves before they hit the street. Breaking the loaves into pieces, Walter would stuff some into his pockets and eat more after the excitement had died down.

When Logé felt his strength returning, he began to pray for another opportunity. How or when it would come he knew not, but one thing was certain—the Russians were not likely to bring him back to Dnepropetrovsk. When he made a break this time, he was determined to gain enough distance to make that impractical.

"I've seen enough of this city," he resolved.

He had not long to wait. One day his group was assigned to a section of the city across the river to the north. Toward four in the afternoon the sky grew dark with angry clouds. In the distance the thunder muttered storm warnings. Lightning flickered across the sky. Still the guard kept the prisoners at their labor. The air, oppressive and heavy, bore down on them. Most of the citizens and military personnel began scurrying for cover; but the guard, ever mindful of his duty, kept the prisoners cleaning bricks. At the first drops of rain everyone scampered for shelter except the guard and his charges. Standing with rifle in hand, he was determined to get as much work out of the men as he could. Some of the prisoners began looking apprehensively at the sky and then questioningly at the guard, but it was no use. He stood watching them work. Why not? The weather might change and the storm pass as quickly as it had come.

Suddenly there was no more waiting to find out. The black clouds unfolded in rapid succession, and within minutes the entire city was wrapped in a fierce storm. Lightning leaped from cloud to cloud and cloud to earth in staccato flashes, followed quickly by sharp claps of thunder. Rain that had been falling in sprinkles suddenly poured from lowering clouds as though someone had slit a giant bag. The deluge caught the guard and prisoners in the open; and, without thinking of their status, all ran for shelter.

Standing along doorways and under eaves, the men pressed for every inch of protection. The guard, rifle barrel down, leaned against a building post with his head lowered to keep the rain from running down his face. Walter and a squatty hunchback stood against a wall watching the guard. They were partially hidden by the pillar. Walter wiped the rain from his face with the back of his hand and looked down the street. It was clear but very risky. The guard would have to turn only a half circle to see in that direction. Walter quickly moved to the edge of the building about twenty feet away and peered around the corner. This too was clear. He made a quick glance toward the guard and was about to run when he realized the hunchback had followed him and was right by his side. He looked down at him, and as their eyes met the little man rocked his head in the same direction Walter had intended to run. His deepset eyes carried a message more eloquently than his hoarse whisper.

"Will you let me go with you?"

Logé hesitated. The poor man with his wild, disheveled hair and contorted body looked so gnomelike and incapable of fleeing that Walter almost shook his head. There was no time to ask about his ability because the full fury of the storm was upon them, and every moment counted. Feeling sorry for him, Walter just nodded and began running with the hunchback right at his heels.

Walter could hear the little man wheezing and blowing behind him as he ran, but he was keeping up. Down one street and then another they fled, stopping only momentarily to catch their breath and then move on.

Suddenly they stopped short, not because they needed a rest, but a huge jag of lightning wavered to the top of a nearby building, illuminating the whole area with a bluish-white brilliance. A crack of thunder followed instantly, so violent that it seemed to shake the pavement. As the wind and rain rampaged on, nature punctuated the storm again and again with the blinding flashes. The two men, soaked and unable to see very far, sloshed block after block without knowing just where they were going.

The street gutters rushing full and swift could not carry the tremendous downpour. Eddies of water swirled madly about the corners, foaming and boiling. At first the fugitives tried avoiding the deeper parts, but later they simply sloshed along in a straight line regardless of depth.

5—S.E.

Walter didn't know how the hunchback was doing, but his own lungs seemed to be on fire. He stopped to throw his head back and suck in air. In a moment the rain had him choking and gasping. The hunchback, with both hands on his knees, was bent over with his back to the wind and the rain. Walter bent down too; and, after his breath became normal, he turned his head toward the hunchback. Water was running off the man's chin in a steady stream. He was such a comical sight that Walter would have laughed outright if he had had the time and energy.

"Let's go," he smiled.

The two raced on, but as they passed a civilian hospital they stopped short. From the second story window they saw a nurse silhouetted against a ward light. She was facing the street.

"Has she seen us?" Walter gasped.

He didn't wait for the hunchback to answer, but now they ran harder than ever. If the nurse had seen them, she really wouldn't know who they were because of the darkness, but she might be suspicious. They were not taking chances.

A few blocks later, where the buildings thinned out, the two escapees came to a concrete sloping ditch about twenty feet deep. Although water was collecting in the bottom, it was definitely not intended for drainage.

"The city tank trap!" exclaimed Walter. "Dnepropetrovsk's base line!"

This would make an ideal escape route. The two slid down the side and began splashing along. They knew now that they were at the west end of the city and by turning right they would be going north away from the river. Eventually this route would lead them to the country.

6

BY THE time the fleeing men climbed out of the tank trap the storm had abated. They had not felt the wind so much in the ditch, but now every breeze was noticeable. Their clothes clung to their soaked skin and made them miserable. They had entered a vast muddy field where walking was difficult. Cold, hungry, and weary from fleeing, they stumbled on through most of the night just to keep warm. Toward dawn they fell utterly exhausted right where they were. Now they could sleep, never mind the conditions. When they awoke, the sun shone brilliantly over acres of young sunflower plants.

The hunchback turned his head away from the eastern

The May Day March

glare and slowly pulled himself to his feet. He did not wait to find out whether or not Logé was awake. "How far do you think we've come?" he asked.

Walter only faintly heard the words. His mind was still too groggy. He felt very old and dull at the moment, and the hunchback had to repeat the question. Walter got to his knees and stood to stretch. One arm had been pinned under him and was asleep. He began swinging it for better circulation.

"Oh, I suppose seventy or seventy-five kilometers," he said, although he was not too articulate when he spoke. "Maybe eighty."

He stopped the arm swinging, tilted his head back, and slowly revolved it to get the kinks out of his neck. "It was a long way, I know."

The hunchback looked around. "Not a house in sight," he said. "We were lucky."

Walter did not answer. He was still too busy unkinking himself.

"I've got some sunflower seeds, a few cabbage leaves I saved from the garbage, and some matches somewhere," the hunchback said, fumbling in his pockets. "We could build a little fire and make some soup."

"No fire!" Walter exclaimed. "That would really be a signal."

"Oh, it's a long way to anyone from here," argued the little man. "Who would see it?"

Walter looked across the expanse. The gently rolling land seemed to extend endlessly in every direction. "I still don't think we should. Someone could be living in a hollow and might turn us in."

The hunchback had found his matches, sunflower seeds, and wilted cabbage leaves. Taking off his shirt, he spread everything on it to dry.

"Everything will go farther if we make a little broth first," he said with an air of finality.

Walter did not feel like arguing, but he did like the idea of getting dry. He began taking off his own clothes and urged the hunchback to finish stripping.

"So long as we are in the drying business we might as well get everything dry."

The sun felt good on their naked bodies. Wisps of vapor rose from their clothes, and as they watched the spots slowly drying, their heads began to nod.

"I wish there were a strawstack around," Walter said slowly. "I feel as if I could sleep and sleep."

The two sat dozing until their clothes had dried. The dry clothes felt good. Walter was ready to depart, and by hurrying the hunchback he hoped to end all talk of building a fire. But it didn't work that way. When they passed a few mud puddles, it started the hunchback on the soup topic again. He begged Walter to stop while he hunted for fragments of dead stalks and weeds. All the time he kept talking about how good the broth would taste.

Walter disagreed. "I'd rather take my chances on finding an isolated farmhouse."

The hunchback seemed not to hear. He stopped and soon had a small fire going, with water on to boil in an old army canteen he carried.

Reluctantly Walter stayed. He was tempted simply to walk away and leave the hunchback to sip his own watery soup.

For the first time since they had been together the hunchback smiled.

"Sit down and relax." He pointed to the broth beginning to steam. "This will make you feel a lot better. Then we can go find a farmhouse."

"I'm not so sure." Walter sat cross-legged on the ground

in front of the fire. The broth idea sounded good, but that line of smoke ascending into the blue made him uneasy.

They had been there only a short while when a voice startled them.

"What are you men doing over there?"

Walter jumped to his feet. The hunchback quickly kicked out the fire, but it was a useless effort. A farmer who had suddenly appeared on the nearest knoll was coming directly toward them. It would be futile for them to try to flee. There might be a whole village just over the rise.

Logé explained to the man that they had escaped, and after a brief exchange of words the farmer led the way back to his house. The fugitives were surprised to discover how near they had been to this dwelling. Walter was tempted to remind the hunchback about his signal fire, but then thought better of it. What did it matter? This might be a short stop anyway.

The farmer was friendly and affable, but Walter could tell he had no intention of allowing them to leave. He detected the farmer's fear of punishment if they were not turned over to the authorities. Walter hoped that at least they wouldn't be returned to Dnepropetrovsk.

"We will have good meals for you while you're at my house," the farmer smiled, "but tomorrow I will have to send you away."

Walter returned the smile. He felt so good about the promise of substantial farm food that he didn't worry about the next day. He tried not to concern himself about the morrow anyway. One day at a time was his philosophy.

The hunchback's facial expressions indicated he did not share in this feeling. He was nervous and fidgety, and tried constantly to catch Walter's attention, signaling with his hands and eyes about escaping from the house. Walter refused to make plans for escaping right then. If the hunchback had not built the fire they would not be in this spot, but now that they were, he wanted to get as much out of it as he could. He enjoyed the farm family's company and began to relax the same as during the German occupation when he had fraternized with the Russians. If these folk had a balalaika he would gladly play and sing for them right now. Throughout the meal the hunchback cast an eye toward Walter and then the door, but Walter was too busy laughing and enjoying himself to bother. He relaxed as if he were an old friend of the family.

That evening while the two men slept on the floor, a teen-ager sat by the door with a rifle across his knee. Walter knew that this would never have been necessary had the hunchback not been with him. The fellow's demeanor before these peasants had certainly not inspired confidence.

Later that evening, when the embers in the fireplace barely illuminated the room, the hunchback awoke and began shaking Walter. "Tell the young fellow I have to leave for the privy."

Walter raised himself up on one elbow and mumbled a few words of Russian to the boy. The boy nodded sleepily and through half-closed eyes fumbled around to open the door without leaving his chair.

When the hunchback returned, the door was still ajar, but the youngster was asleep. Immediately taking in the situation, the hunchback tiptoed to Walter and bent over to whisper in his ear.

"Psst. Come on. Let's go!"

Walter understood, but he barely opened his eyes. Turning his head from side to side, he indicated that he was not going.

The hunchback thought Walter was not fully awake and risking detection from the teen-ager he whispered hoarsely, "Let's go."

Walter shook his head again. "No," he whispered, "I'm not leaving."

The hunchback grunted his disapproval and waved a hand downward in disgust. Walter watched him slip out the door and into the night.

"I'm glad he is gone," Walter sighed to himself. "I only tried to help him in the first place."

While there was some concern the next morning over the escape of the hunchback, the farmer was pleased when Walter said he would not flee. He smiled as he assured his host, "You needn't worry; I'll let you do your duty."

The farmer was so congenial that after a breakfast of eggs, bread, and milk he unwrapped one of his carefully guarded cigarettes and offered it to Walter.

"No thanks. I don't smoke."

The farmer's eyebrows raised in unbelief. "You don't smoke?"

Walter tried to explain his reasons for not smoking, but the man just shook his head. Refuse such a luxury, such a rarity?

The farmer's son was instructed to deliver Walter to the nearest village; and as the two left the yard, Walter turned to wave good-bye. The man stood in the doorway with his wife. Both were smiling, but the farmer put his fingers to his mouth as if he were smoking and then shook his head again.

Walter had a full stomach. The sun warmed him through, and a sense of well-being made him want to join the birds in singing. It mattered not that he was being escorted under armed guard to the village or that he was really headed northward instead of westward. He knew the kind hand of Providence would open the way for him to continue his westward journey when the time came. Logically he should have escaped with the hunchback, but he had no relish for that man's companionship; and for some reason he did not wish to betray the trust of the kind peasants who had fed him, even though he knew they would turn him in. He would not worry. If God could take care of him inside Russia, He could also watch over his family in Berlin. By watchfulness, prayer, and determination he would eventually be reunited with them. He began to sing lustily. The teen-ager grinned as Walter turned his head and beckoned him to his side.

"Come on up beside me," Walter invited as he interrupted his song.

The boy hesitated, but as Walter continued singing, the boy quickened his pace.

Walter stopped singing again and winked. "You didn't need to bring that rifle along."

The boy was still grinning. "I suppose not, but I was told to."

Walter laughed. "I won't run away from you."

At the village the farmer boy turned Logé over to the local deputy. He, in turn, secured another teen-age guard to conduct the fugitive to the next village in the direction of Krasnograd.

The message of the prisoner's jovial attitude was relayed from escort to escort. Every teen-ager that went with Walter sooner or later walked right by his side. To each he had the same remark: "You don't need a rifle with me."

It wasn't that they doubted him; each one carried a rifle because it would be rather hard to explain to the authorities why any citizen without a gun would attempt to deliver an escapee.

After two days of relays and passing through five villages Walter was finally turned over to a Russian officer at the Krasnograd prison camp on the outskirts of the city. The moment he saw the rows and rows of brick barracks within the barbed wire, he wondered how far he would have been had he followed the hunchback. It was only a fleeting thought. He had so conditioned himself to live for the present that he had few regrets about staying with the peasants. Why worry? He had escaped four times before; he could do it again. True, he had been successful only half the time, but he had come a long way since Makeyevka.

Krasnograd, however, was not just another prison camp. It was mostly a collection point for ex-escapees, the last stop before shipment to Siberia. Designed especially to keep would-be-escape attempts to a minimum, it had a coal mine three miles from camp which occupied fourteen hours a day for both men and women. For particularly obstreperous prisoners there was "the closet," a cubicle too narrow for anyone to sit comfortably, and too low to stand. Twice a day the Russians would bring the prisoner out of this torture box for food, water, and toilet, then return him. This device helped bring about full cooperation and obedience to prison regulations.

Walter was led to the commandant, a pompous little red-faced man who obviously tried to be impressive before others. Taking off his slipper, he struck Walter full in the face. Walter's cheek soon matched the color of the commandant's face.

"Trying to escape, eh? What's your name?"

"Logé, Walter Logé."

The commandant seemed puzzled. "Hmmm. French," he muttered.

Walter was inwardly amused. His ancestry along that line was a long way back, but for now it was a good classification.

"We have all nationalities here," the commandant said arrogantly, "but they soon learn that it does not pay to escape. I promise you Krasnograd can keep you in line." Then holding both hands in front of him he motioned with his fingers. "Now give me your belt."

Walter had worn out his belt and was using an old piece of rope instead. He untied this and handed it to the commandant.

"This will be returned when you are prepared for work," the commandant said.

Walter was taken to the "processing" room on the second floor. It was filled with people, and as one of the guards opened the door, the stuffy air with its human odors was so strong that it made Walter recoil. He had never seen such crowded conditions before. Men and women were squeezed so tightly that they had to take turns to sit. He spent nearly a week in this miserable room holding his sagging trousers and trying desperately to get a little sleep. Aside from the impossible sleeping positions available, there were the incessant moans and crying from those who suffered. Relief came only twice a day when they were lined up for food, water, and the privy. The only difference between this and "the closet" was the possibility of sitting occasionally and always the opportunity to stand. When they finally ordered Walter to work, he was weak and exhausted from the ordeal but happy to be able to do something besides waste away in an overcrowded room. The coal mine couldn't be worse.

In the next few days, however, he almost changed his mind. Krasnograd lived up to its sordid reputation. Aside from the morning and evening walk to and from the coal mine, there wasn't much fresh air during the twenty-four hours. The barracks were always foul, and the coal mine could hardly be considered refreshing.

Walter was assigned work at the 800-foot level. Descending via a rickety platform elevator with no guard railing was only the first of his encounters with the hazards of the mine. Only the foremen wore hard hats with lights. Aside from the main corridor leading to the shaft there were no lights anywhere in the mine. Without headgear the slave laborers were expected to protect themselves as best they could and to work in the dark, cramped quarters shoveling the unseen chunks. Walter soon learned why so many appeared in the evening with bloody head wounds and facial abrasions. Without constant vigilance the hapless slaves were always subject to collisions with the dark interior. Often he could hear the women sobbing in some far-off corner while they tried to continue filling their work quota after being hurt.

This was not all. The mine officers were never too careful about notifying the prisoners before explosions. A charge would be set, and without warning the blast would rock the mine. When the sound of rumbling had died away, Walter often heard someone moaning or crying in the distance.

Krasnograd was all that the commandant had promised. It was the worst Walter had ever seen. Every time he passed the old white horse pulling coal cars to the loading shaft on his level, he thought about it. There was a sympathetic, mutual tie. The poor creature had not seen the light of day for years. With drooping head and tired muscles he was forced to pull the heavy loads throughout the long, dreary hours.

"I'll soon be in the same shape if I don't get out of here," thought Walter.

It seemed impossible. He was so tired after a few days of work that he could only gulp down his meal and drag himself to the hard bunk. There was no time to plan an escape or think of anything but drudgery. In a short while he felt himself slipping into that numbness that soon erases all hope. It frightened him to realize how quickly he could fall into this mental abyss and become so paralyzed.

With all of his strength Logé tried to think about home, Berlin, family. Every mental picture was an effort. He wanted to sleep, just sleep. The next day would come all too soon. The morning meal, the walk to work, and then shoveling coal down a chute all day. Shoveling, shoveling till he was nothing more than a machine. His muscles quivered involuntarily. He felt so drained that nothing seemed important but resting. In the recesses of his mind, though, he felt that he must get his old drive back. He must think —pray.

May 1, 1945, dawned like any other day to the prisoners of Krasnograd. Most of them had lost all track of time. The citizens of the city, however, had not forgotten. May Day is always significant for those within the USSR; but this year, with the certainty of Hitler's downfall so near, the atmosphere seemed charged with expectancy. Everyone was primed for the festivities. There were to be banners and bunting, music and marching, vodka and laughter.

Walter was not feeling well that morning. Afflicted with diarrhea and abdominal pains, he wondered how he would ever complete his work quota. He didn't try to think about it, but the fourteen hours stretched before him in a miserable mental tableau. He reached his hand for the damp wall, rested his head against his arm, and sighed audibly.

"Oh, God! God, give me strength—the old fight."

Within an hour he was so doubled over with pain that he knew he would have to report to the foreman. The outcome could mean punishment, but he would have to risk it. This time he didn't even pat the old white horse in the corridor. Making his way to the shaft, he found the foreman standing by the elevator switch watching him approach.

The officer frowned. "Sick?" But there was something in his voice that indicated he knew Walter was not feigning.

Walter nodded. "I can't work. I have stomach cramps and diarrhea."

The foreman jerked his thumb toward the elevator. "I'll send you up to see the camp doctor."

When Walter reached the mine entrance, he walked slowly past the shower room. Here the prisoners were given the privilege of cleaning up every evening. A warm shower might make him feel better right now, but on second thought he decided to see the doctor first.

The camp clinic was on the far edge of the small mine compound next to the barbed wire. He walked up the steps and knocked. The only response was a hoarse woman's voice from within. "Come."

Walter stepped inside and faced a plump, broad-shouldered woman in a white uniform.

"What you got?" she asked brusquely.

"Diarrhea—cramps."

She mumbled something under her breath as she went to the medicine cabinet. Obviously she had little or no time for prisoners, especially on this day. Fumbling with a few boxes and reading labels on the jars, she finally found the thing she wanted. Pouring out the pills into an envelope, she sealed it with her tongue and handed it to Walter.

"Here, take these, and make them last all day." She bent over her desk, and scribbled something on a piece of paper. She handed it to Walter. "This is your pass. Go back to the barracks and sleep the rest of the day."

For a moment Walter looked at the scribbling. He couldn't read Russian, but if this was what the doctor said it was, she had unwittingly handed him his freedom.

"Thank you," he said. He closed the clinic door and walked away.

As he approached the main gate, he noticed it was decorated with a red flag. He walked up to the guard and showed him the pass.

"What's the occasion?" Walter asked.

"Don't you know?" He raised his eyebrows in apparent surprise. "This is May Day."

"Oh!" Walter smiled feebly.

The guard glanced at the doctor's signature on the pass and handed it back to Walter. He would need it to get into the prison camp.

Walter took the pass and the packet of pills he had been holding in his hand and put them into his chest pocket. The great wire gate swung open, supposedly to allow the prisoner to walk back to the barracks to recuperate, but Walter knew he was free. All thoughts of getting a shower vanished. Suddenly his mind was strangely alert. That phlegmatic feeling disappeared even though the stomach cramps stayed with him. Perhaps this was for the best right then. As he walked away from the mine enclosure he was forced to stop and bend over with pain a few times.

He knew there were several pairs of guard's eyes watching him depart, so he did not want to rush anyway. It must look natural, and the pain kept him from being overly anxious. His mind was running at top speed now, sifting through every idea that pressed itself to the fore. How to take advantage of this? How? How to make a break from dreaded Krasnograd without having every guard and officer in the whole mine area hunting him?

In the distance Walter could hear music. A band played and people sang.

"May Day—so that's it," he said to himself. Then suddenly the idea came. He must not hurry until he was completely out of sight of the mine. He had it, he thought. He had it! His heart pounded with excitement. A parade! His big chance!

The moment he was out of range of inquisitive eyes he dropped over the side of the road and ran along the ditch in search of a mud puddle. He would need water. He felt vibrant with the scheme. Pain and illness seemed lost as he felt a new surge of energy. Finding a puddle that had backed up by a clump of willows, he reached into the inner pocket of his clothes and took out the old collapsible army razor and five blades he had secreted back at Makeyevka. The blades had rusted, so it would make no difference which one he used.

"I've got to shave, though. I must look presentable."

He splashed water over his face, but at the first stroke of the razor he felt as if he had pulled off a layer of skin.

He groaned. "No soap, no hot water—this will be hard going."

He splashed more water over his face and bent over to use the puddle for a mirror. Pulling, jerking, nicking, he shaved as best he could. Trickles of blood ran down his cheeks. Finally he finished and rinsed his face.

Then Walter began to undress. As he did so, he chuckled aloud. "She never knew how much I would need these two sets of clothes. What a good trade!"

He took off his filthy coal-stained outer clothes, and the other suit underneath; then he put them back on in reverse order. The clothes he now wore outside were wrinkled and smelly, but they would be better than the telltale outfit used in the mine. Fortunately he had found a part of an old sheet at Dnepropetrovsk and had fashioned underwear from this by tearing a hole in the top for his head, so the green Russian summer uniform was not as soiled as it might have been. He cleaned off his cap by brushing it in the grass, smoothed his hair back, and looked himself over in the water.

"Not bad," he laughed. "Not bad at all."

Instead of taking the periphery road outside the city that went to the prison camp, Logé headed directly for Krasnograd. The parade was obviously coming his way. The music grew louder and louder, and the very tempo made him hurry faster toward it.

Blood from his shaving cuts had congealed, leaving dark-red spots on Walter's face and neck; but he was positive the people would only think he had been getting ready for the celebration.

"Which I have," he reminded himself.

Walter knew his clothes would pass. He looked no worse than many of the peasants he had seen. As he approached a small open market, he decided to put it to a test. He needed a little nourishment anyway. "There might not be a better time to spend my money than now," he told himself, "even in a bazaar."

He bought himself a bottle of milk and drank it on the spot. Wiping his mouth with the back of his hand, he smiled and walked toward the music. By keeping his words few he had aroused no suspicion. Now he knew his plan could work. The parade was much closer now. He walked several more blocks and, rounding a corner, he saw the whole parade coming directly toward him. In the front ranks people carried huge pictures of Lenin and Stalin, followed by those with great Red flags and banners. Next came the band and behind this a motley crowd of marchers singing with the music.

The escaped prisoner waited calmly on the sidewalk and watched as the procession approached. As it passed, he waved and sang along with everyone else. His timing had to

6—S.E.

be just right. Now? Not quite. The last of the marchers were approaching. He kept waving and singing. With excitement running high and the spirit of the parade at the right pitch, not one Russian had given Walter a second glance so far as he knew. Now! He slipped into the last row and quickly took his place. The man next to him turned his head slightly and smiled.

Walter returned the smile. "Hello," he said, and began singing at the top of his lungs.

The parade continued down the street and toward the city limits. Walter swung his arms and kept in step with the music. He knew some of the national songs and sang as lustily as any of the Russians. Right then he was glad to be identified with them.

Gradually the procession began to disintegrate. One by one the marchers waved good-bye as they left for further festivities in their homes. More and more marchers turned aside, rolling up banners and taking them away to be used another year. Still Walter walked on and on until only a few remained. Never looking to the right or left, he continued down the road until he marched alone. He did not look back until sure that he was far enough away. When he did stop, Krasnograd lay in the distance, shimmering in the early afternoon sun.

Suddenly Walter Logé felt like singing something else. It would be a long time before the evening prison count, and he wanted to rejoice. He threw his head back and shouted from a thankful heart, "The blessing of the Lord has opened the door!"

The horrors of Krasnograd lay behind; the fugitive had plenty of time; and before him stretched the open road for miles and miles. He hadn't felt so happy for a long time.

7

IN THE distance Logé heard a train whistle, and as its prolonged wail died an idea came to him. Why not try riding the train? It would be a bold move, but no greater than the one he had just completed. If he could get on and off a train without detection, he could put much greater distance between him and the Krasnograd prison.

From the top of a rise he could see a main road running at right angles. He intended to turn left when he reached this and head in the direction of the train whistle, but suddenly he stopped. Off to his right he heard another sound. Voices—young voices, singing. He listened carefully. It wasn't the singing that arrested his attention so much as

Dried Leaves Before the Fire

the music. It was not a Russian national song, but something he had sung himself years ago in a young people's meeting in his church in Berlin.

"I know that song!" he exclaimed. "It's 'Always Cheerful'!"

It warmed his heart just to hear it again, and he quickened his pace. By the time he reached the intersection, he met six gaily dressed teen-age girls coming toward him. All were happily singing while one strummed a balalaika. Walter waved as they approached. Their bright costumes, black braided hair with ribbons, and smiling faces presented a pleasant contrast to the drab scenes of the prison.

"Mind if I join you?" he called cheerfully.

The girls laughed. "Sure, sure, come with us!" one of them said.

He held out his hand to the girl with the balalaika. She understood and grinned as she handed it to him.

"I used to play one of these," he said. "Let's see if I can remember."

He put his fingers on the strings and started strumming with the other hand, changing keys several times before singing, "Always Cheerful." Their mouths dropped open in unbelief; then they laughingly joined him in singing.

"Always cheerful, always cheerful,
Sunshine all around I see;
Full of beauty is the path of duty,
Cheerful we will always be."

Walter had to sprinkle the song with a little German, but the girls did not seem to notice.

When they stopped singing, one of the girls looked intently at Walter, her black eyes snapping with curiosity. "Are you a Baptist?"

Walter shook his head and smiled. He wanted to find

out about the girls, but here they were beating him to the question.

"A Seventh-day Adventist?" the girl asked.

Walter nodded his head vigorously.

Two of the girls danced around the group, laughing and clapping their hands. Then they began laughing together, their young voices rippling in high glee.

Walter thought he knew even before asking the question, but he wanted to be sure. "Are you Adventists too?"

"Yes, yes!" they chorused.

Walter Logé had stumbled onto fellow believers just after escaping from the worst prison camp he had ever seen. It was too good to be true, yet there they were, all six of them. His mind raced back to that time in the early thirties when he had found his own faith in a young people's meeting. A tide of nostalgia swept over him—all the glad times together, meeting his wife, singing and being together. And now these happy youngsters. They laughed and sang together the choruses and gospel songs both he and they knew. Eyes flashing, hands clapping, red ribbons and black braids tossing, everyone singing while Walter played. A German escapee surrounded by Russian lassies singing and walking along together. This was Walter's high day, and he felt about as happy as he could remember feeling. Everything seemed to be going his way. It was enough to be able to slip away from Krasnograd, but finding these teen-age fellow Christians was like a delicious dessert after a wonderful meal.

When the girls came to a fork in the road that led to their village, they stopped. "Come home with us," they begged.

It was a tremendous temptation. Walter would love to meet their families, to sing some more, to eat with them. But he shook his head. "It would not be safe for either of us. I've just escaped, and the authorities will be hunting me very soon."

The girls looked sadly at each other, then at Walter. He explained to them about his flight out of their country. He tried to tell them how dangerous it would be to stay even one night in their village. They understood, but it was such a sudden end to a good time.

"You pray for me, won't you?"

The girls nodded.

"My home's in Berlin, and I have a long way to go." He smiled. "We'd better keep that our secret."

The girls nodded again.

"You can help me," he said as he glanced down the main road and then back at them. "How do I get to the nearest train station?"

The girls all began talking at once, but he put together their bits of information and hoped he had them straight. As he waved good-bye, he called back to them, "We have a secret, you know."

They waved for the last time, and as Walter turned and walked away he prayed. He would probably never see those radiant faces again.

" . . . but I want to meet them again, Lord, in that better land. Thank You for letting me have this contact with those Christian young people just this once. I will pray for them, and they will pray for me. Now I know there are Christian believers in Russia. Thank You, Lord."

The experience had stirred depths of his emotions, and the old drive to see his family returned with vigor.

"To see my 'Jewel' again—just to see her!"

It had been a long time since Walter had spoken that favorite nickname he had given his youthful sweetheart.

Now the sound of it made him still more determined. The brief Krasnograd experience had almost made the name slip from his memory, but now he could visualize her slender form waiting in the doorway for him. He smiled to himself just thinking about her quick, happy laughter and those deep, brown, expressive eyes. He was going home—home to his "Jewel."

To Walter this May Day's happenings had been more than just coincidental. The assurance of answered prayer made him that much more confident that he would reach Berlin at last. Whatever was in store for him, all would work out for the best.

It took several hours to reach the train station, and by the time Walter arrived, swarms of people were already boarding trains. There were three tracks, each occupied by a train, but the middle one was filling fast. The fugitive made his way between the cars and, without asking questions, took the fourth car from the end. Although he saw no guards posted, he knew the Russians usually had one riding at each end of the train. He wanted to be far enough from them when he jumped off.

The seats filled rapidly, and then people began using the large overhead racks to lie down. Walter took one nearest the vestibule and curled up. He felt fairly safe. The typical Russian wartime travel conditions minimized the risk of any authority asking for papers or tickets en route.

Two hours later the train finally jerked forward toward an unknown destination. Walter wondered if some strange fate might bring him back to Krasnograd; but as the train headed slowly out of the railroad yards, he was relieved. The sun, gently slipping beyond the horizon, seemed to be the lodestone toward which the engine headed. He smiled to himself and closed his eyes.

It had been quite a day, one Walter Logé would never forget. There had been rumors in Russia that Hitler was dead, and Walter sensed that the conflict in Europe should be almost over. Yet his own battle for freedom was a long way from the finish.

The air was hot and stuffy inside, and the low murmuring of many passengers and the soporific effect of clicking wheels soon lulled the weary escapee to sleep.

Walter was too cramped to stay asleep long. He stretched his legs out over the space above the aisle and slipped down. He wanted to stay awake anyway. The whole night might pass away and they would suddenly pull into a station where the authorities would check each passenger. He walked to the platform between the cars and positioned himself by the steel gate. Leaning his head against the car, he relaxed, but he did not allow himself to slumber.

In the early predawn hours the train slowed to a crawl. It had never moved very rapidly at any time, but the change of tempo alerted Walter to his opportunity. He peered outside. He saw no lights except the one wobbling on the nose of the engine probing the rails ahead. He craned his head around to see if a guard might be watching from a high observation post on the last car. Nothing.

Walter smiled. "If he's back there, he'll be asleep. Russians are such heavy sleepers this time of day."

The train was moving so slowly he knew a jump would not hurt. One final look. Now was the time. He leaped wide, sprawling quickly on his face and flattening his body. Not a shout or a shot. The train creaked and groaned by, leaving him alone and panting heavily against the earth. Walter waited until the sound of the train had died away before getting up.

"I don't know where I am," Walter said as he brushed the front of his clothes, "but that was a lot better than walking all night."

Faint gray from the eastern sky gave him enough visibility to pick his way across a sunflower field without stumbling. Weary and terribly hungry, he moved on, hoping to find a resting place. Before seeking food Walter knew he would have to sleep.

Dawn, running its fingers of light through the last remnant of night, made the whole countryside sensitive with anticipation of another day. The cool calmness of that hour was refreshing. Walter stopped and breathed deeply, filling his lungs with the invigorating air.

"Too bad I'm so tired," he said. "This would be a good time to keep walking."

He came to the brow of a hill and saw below him the dark outline of a grove. When he descended, he found himself within a lovely tree-studded village. Dried leaves had collected in a long drainage ditch that ran along the outskirts. Where debris and limbs had blocked the passage, the leaves had washed into great heaps.

Walter had an idea. Finding one of the larger piles, he gathered a few more for good measure and crawled inside. Adjusting a small breathing hole, he soon began to drowse. It was comfortable and quiet, and within minutes he was oblivious to surroundings. When he awoke, the sun was high and the warmth of his nest made it so cozy he felt like sleeping for a few more hours. He hadn't been so deliciously warm since that time in the strawstack. Only here there were no mice. Suddenly, however, he heard something that made his heart pound with excitement and forced the thought of resting from his mind.

"Raz, dva, tri, chetire—"

"Oh, no!" Walter uttered half aloud.

The cadence count of an army officer as he marched his contingent along the top of the ditch drew closer and closer.

"Raz, dva, tri, chetire—"

Walter scooted down farther in his leaf bed. His drowsiness vanished, and his muscles tightened. They were right above him now. The commanding officer suddenly barked an order that sent a chill right through him.

"Split apart, and hit the ditch!"

Walter seemed to feel his blood congeal as he realized that the soldiers might have bayonets and start practicing on any soft-looking objects. Silently he prayed. Soldiers scrambled all about him, and he heard one drop right next to his own pile of leaves. Walter could hear him breathing hard as he fingered his rifle trigger and began going through the motions of firing imaginary rounds at an invisible enemy. He was so close that Walter feared to breathe.

"All right, back on the line!" the officer shouted.

The soldiers leaped to their feet at the command and resumed their positions above the ditch. As the men marched back to their own barracks, Walter slowly let the air out of his lungs. The brief mock firing maneuvers so near his sleeping quarters made his mouth dry. The heap of leaves had been too close to the fire as far as he was concerned. He crawled out, flushed and hot.

"Thank—You—God," he stammered audibly.

8

WALTER knocked on the door of the nearest house. His hunger and thirst drives were so strong that it didn't matter to him just who answered. Fortunately he was greeted by a kindly Ukrainian woman whose very obesity radiated a friendliness. Her dark eyes, set deep in layers of fat, danced with excitement as this stranger announced he was an escapee and needed food and drink. News and non-routine events were scarce in her village, and she welcomed Walter as if he had been a member of the family.

"Come in, come in. I'll get you something warm right away." She motioned the fugitive toward a seat while she bustled about with the food. "We hear only what they tell

Food to Share With Soldiers

us over the village loudspeaker. You must have more news than this."

Walter nodded. "I don't think they would ever tell you about the prison camps they have."

"Tell me."

Walter began to unravel the whole story, starting at Makeyevka without naming the city. He avoided all references to Krasnograd. This would be too dangerous until he was much farther away.

Customarily the woman would have invited her neighbors over to hear choice news, but she was so entranced by the story that she forgot everything else but listening and getting the meal. She plied her unusual guest with a continuous volley of questions, and it soon became apparent that her inquisitiveness was matched only by Walter's voracious appetite. She sat down across from him with her elbows on the table and her hands folded in front of her, listening in rapt attention while he talked and finished the last of the potatoes, bread, and soup. She pushed a dish of platski toward him, trying to prolong the meal. The pressed sunflower cakes tasted good to Walter; and, following the Russian custom, he leaned back in his chair and systematically spat the hulls on the floor. The woman would sweep these outside after the meal.

Walter talked on for several minutes; then, finishing, he patted his stomach and smiled. "I appreciate this so much."

The woman returned his smile. "Don't mention it. It has been a long time since I have had a man here to eat." For a moment she turned toward the window. Her eyes looked sad and far away. "My husband has been away to the war for three years now, and there is no word."

Walter stood to leave. "It can't be long now," he said. "Then he will be coming back"—he looked right into her eyes, trying hard to encourage her—"just as I am going to get back to Berlin. A man needs to be home."

He stood in the doorway a moment before getting directions and saying good-bye. "Thank you. Thanks so much! Every little bit along the way helps."

The woman waved as the fugitive walked along the route she had directed away from the army post. It had been a pleasant encounter for both of them.

Walter knew that with warmer weather coming on he would have to have more water, and he hated to stop at a house every time he was thirsty. He had long ago lost the tin can and string he had owned at Makeyevka. It had never been too successful, but if he placed a small pebble in the can for weight it would do. Stopping by the village garbage dump, he selected another American-made tin can and gouged a hole near the top. He found pieces of string and old strands of rope to tie together for lowering it into a well. He also found an old potato sack he could use to carry food.

Walter had walked perhaps fifteen or twenty miles to the next village when he had to stop for a drink. The well was deep, and he spent several minutes just getting a little water. His persistence prolonged the affair far beyond normal, but he continued trying. Finally, when he straightened himself and was about to walk away, a well-dressed man in a buggy called to him.

"Come on; I'll give you a lift."

"Oh, no!" Walter groaned within himself. Something about the voice indicated that his freedom ended here.

Reluctantly Walter climbed up beside the man and gave a weak smile. The man clucked to his horse, and the buggy moved toward the village center.

"You must have been very thirsty," the man said without looking toward Walter.

"Very."

"You've escaped from somewhere, haven't you?"

Walter nodded. "Yes, I have escaped." He wished he had shaved at the woman's house and had not spent so much time at the well.

"What's your name?"

"Walter Logé."

"Then you're a Frenchman?"

"Way back."

The man looked intently at Walter. "The authorities are scouring the country for an escaped Hungarian."

Walter unconsciously rolled his eyes toward the man. His mouth went dry. Could it be that the Krasnograd officials were on the prowl for him this far away? Was he the "Hungarian" they were after? His heart began to race at the thought.

"I want you to come home with me for a while," the man said. "I'll have to do a little phoning." He paused and smiled. "And I will give you a good drink of water."

Walter felt thirsty again, but he could easily have passed this offer by. With a sigh he settled back and relaxed and slowly resigned himself to his fate.

After a brief telephone conversation it was decided to deliver Walter to the next village deputy. When Walter saw the man, he felt completely at ease, even though he was promptly informed that the military police were coming. The elderly gentleman had such a benign look and soft-spoken manner that had he announced a return trip to Krasnograd, Walter would hardly have felt nervous about it.

When the jeep with the two MP's arrived, however, the old man could not persuade them to take Walter. They looked at the escapee and shook their heads.

"No, we're not interested in him," they said. "He's not the Hungarian."

The wrinkles on the deputy's face deepened as he spoke with determination. "But you have to take him."

The MP's were adamant. "We won't take into custody anyone not on our list."

As they drove off, the deputy turned to Walter and smiled.

"I guess you stay with me a few days until I can decide what to do with you."

Walter smiled too. This might not be a bad thing. He would get enough food for his next try anyway. He secretly hoped for something else though. The more he scratched the more he thought about it.

"I've got too much of a partnership with these lice," he said to himself. "It would be good if I could get a bath here."

There was a small civilian hospital behind the deputy's house, and the next day Walter decided the best way to get to clean up would be to offer his services.

"Could I do some work in the hospital?" he asked.

The deputy raised his eyebrows. "Just what could you do?"

"Oh, I've been in the medical corps. I can work as an orderly, take care of the dressings—about anything that needs doing."

The deputy was interested. He escorted Walter to the hospital and, after conversing with the authorities, decided to put him on the ward helping the shorthanded staff.

It was a crude hospital with straw ticks for mattresses and few modern facilities. During the warm spring days many of the beds had been placed outside, giving the appearance that the institution was falling apart at the seams.

Much to Walter's dismay, the hospital staff didn't even ask him to clean up, but put him to work as he was, changing dressings and serving meals from the large kettle in the kitchen. The hospital did provide him with food, but because of bed shortage he was told to sleep at the deputy's house.

During the next few days both the patients and staff seemed to respond to his smiles and pleasantries. He was just getting well acquainted when the deputy announced the end of the stay.

"Tomorrow I am having a man deliver you to the next village. You can't remain here indefinitely. We will have to keep relaying you until the army or someone takes you over."

On his last day of work Walter found an opportunity to get a little cash. He sold his outer garments for a few rubles just in case he needed something in an emergency. Brushing the coal dust from his blue clothes as best he could, he thought to himself, "Now with just one pair of summer wear I must make it to Berlin before winter."

May 8, 1945—VE Day! As Walter and the relay man approached the next village, the bells from the old Orthodox church rang out over the countryside. The whole town seemed in festive mood. Because there were no placards and pictures as in the May Day celebration, Walter thought it was just some local occasion. In a few minutes he was to become involved in one of the strangest happenings in his long trek out of Russia.

At the edge of the village two soldiers came from a side road. The relay man tried to get them to take charge of Walter. But, just as the MP's had done a few days before, the soldiers refused. They were also looking for the Hungarian, and would not take anyone else. So the relay man turned to Walter and said firmly, "Follow them anyhow. This is as far as I can go, and there isn't anyone else to take you."

Walter blinked in astonishment. He would head in their

direction, but if they walked away from him, he certainly wasn't going to put forth an honest effort to keep up. He was about half a block behind the soldiers when a crowd burst from the church and surged down the hill toward the gaily decorated bazaar. Sweeping by the market, where they collected all sorts of foodstuffs, they began laughing and singing in gay anticipation of a feast. When they saw Walter slowly trudging toward them, they surged forward in one accord and surrounded him. Someone took the old potato sack he carried and began filling it. Others joined, and in moments Walter found himself the recipient of fruits, cakes, bread, and a few bottles of milk. Was this a dream? What could it all mean? In his soiled Russian military blues he might have given them the appearance of one of their own returning from the war. Whatever their motives Walter was certainly weighted down with more than he could eat at one time, and almost more than he could carry.

When the soldiers saw the commotion, they rushed back to disperse the crowd. "Move away, move away!" they shouted.

"Why? Why?" the crowd demanded. "He's a blessing to us. It's all over, you know!"

Walter had not heard the news and still could not make anything out of the jumble of happy voices. He thought maybe the people had come from the church to distribute things to the poor.

As the last of the crowd dispersed, Walter turned to the soldiers. "Don't you men want some of this?" he offered.

One of the soldiers with a cigarette dangling from his lips shook his head. "We can't accept anything until we find our man. We're allowed only iron rations until we get him."

He motioned his comrade to lead the way out of the village.

"You'd better come with us until we get you out of here. We'll take you to the next village anyway."

Walter, his shoulder already aching from holding the heavy sack of food, was sure he could not walk very far. He tried to keep up with the soldiers, but they slowly pulled away until he could not close the gap. Long after they had left the village and toward evening he felt that he could not take another step.

"Wait up!" he called. "Let's stop and eat."

The soldiers waited for him, but their leader again shook his head. "No, we can't eat, or we'd get in trouble. We have been assigned to find a Hungarian escapee, and we're not supposed to have full meals until we find him."

Walter lowered the heavy sack and rested it against the front of his legs. "I can't carry all this food much farther. I'm not the Hungarian, but I am an escapee." He pointed toward a nearby strawstack in a field. "Let's go over there and rest and eat supper."

"Maybe to rest, but not to eat," the soldier said, but his voice was not convincing. Walter could tell both men were weakening.

When the men settled themselves against the strawstack, Walter spread all the food before them. The soldiers sat looking at all the variety like little children in a candy store. One licked his lips and tried to turn his gaze away.

Walter knew the soldiers had not eaten a decent meal for a long time, and he wanted to share with them. "Now help yourselves," he said.

They shook their heads.

Walter bowed his head and offered grace in German while the soldiers stared.

"What was that for?" one of them asked.

"I was asking God to bless the food for our supper. I can't pray very well in Russian."

The soldiers looked at each other incredulously.

Walter broke off several pieces of bread and handed some to them. "Now eat; you can't do your work without eating."

The soldiers could resist no longer. Suddenly they began eating as if it might be their last meal. Walter greatly enjoyed the whole affair. Here was plenty of good food, and sharing this with these Russian soldiers only heightened the pleasure. While they ate, he began telling of his escapes and all the providential leadings. It was obvious the soldiers enjoyed this as much as the food. They often stopped eating and just smiled at each other.

With appetite satisfied, one of the soldiers reached into his jacket pocket and offered Walter a cigarette. "This is all we have to share," he said.

"No thanks. I don't smoke."

"You don't smoke?" they chorused.

"No, I never have. I honestly don't think God can bless that."

The soldier took the cigarette and put it to his own lips. "You must be a religious man."

"I am a weak man, I know." Walter began gathering up the remainder of the food and putting it into the sack. "I may have to have you help me carry this."

The soldier handed his comrade a cigarette. They sat there smoking leisurely and looking at Walter. The one that had offered Walter the cigarette smiled. "We'll have to tell our superior about you. I don't think we will be punished for eating after he hears how it happened." He turned his head and smiled at his companion. "This is the first good meal we've had in a week."

They stood and shook hands with Walter before moving on. That evening the three walked until it was too dark to see, and then they slept in an open field. They continued on all the next day until sundown. By then they had consumed nearly all of Walter's food. Weary from walking, they made their way to a train station in a forested area on the outskirts of a town. The elongated shadow patterns cast by the trees seemed to make aisles leading to the lights on the train. The soldiers elbowed their way inside the train and made several passengers move out of the way.

"Make room for this man," they said. "We have to serve him. He is a good man."

Walter felt embarrassed about all this attention. He did not know how to react. The soldiers began telling all the civilians in the car about their experience with Walter. Everyone listened intently as the soldiers retold of his escapes. One old peasant woman was so impressed that she came over to Walter. Placing a bottle of milk before him, she whispered, "Oh, you're such a nice person."

The train moved away slowly into the night. Walter was never certain about the direction they were traveling, but one thing was sure—their destination would prove very interesting.

9

SHORTLY after five o'clock in the morning the train eased into a station. Before Walter realized it had stopped, one of the soldiers gently shook him.

"Wake up," the soldier urged. "We're at the base now."

Walter raised his head and blinked. He had slept so long with his arms folded in front of him that it was difficult to move. For a brief moment he could not remember where he was. Another day had been pressed upon him, and he rubbed his eyes trying to recollect what had happened.

"Come on, we're here," the soldier repeated.

Walter shook his head and got up to follow the soldiers to the rear of the car. As he stepped onto the platform, he

To Be a Popular Prisoner

could see in the distance a vast army camp with rows of brick barracks. It was really not far to walk, but that morning he felt very tired and weak. With all the food he had had within the past few days, he knew it could have done little to make up for the weight loss since his original capture. Even though he carried no load, he was unable to keep up with the soldiers, who often had to stop and wait for him.

Upon arrival at camp, the two soldiers took their charge immediately to the toilet where others were already cleaning up before breakfast. Walter knew enough of Russian customs to practice their morning awakening exercise. He stepped up to the sink and filled his mouth with water, then spit it into his hands, rubbing it rapidly over his face. He did this vigorously six or seven times and then used the last mouthful to wet his hands for brushing his hair. The soldiers who had brought Walter smiled at him. "You're just like a Russian," one remarked.

Walter was next taken to headquarters, and as they approached the building one of the soldiers motioned for him to sit. "Wait here on the steps," he smiled. "We will be back shortly."

Another man was sitting there, his head buried in his hands. He seemed to be the epitome of dejection.

Walter sat in silence watching the man. He was about to go over and find out what was the matter when the door swung open. A high-ranking officer strode out, followed by the two soldiers at his heels. He did not glance at Walter, but went straight for the other man. The officer grabbed the poor man's collar and jerked him to his feet and then gave him a swift backhanded slap full in the face. The man's head swung backwards from the impact, and in self defense he bent over, holding both hands over his face for protection.

"You have caused us enough trouble!" the officer snarled. "Hungarian! Gypsy!" He spat out the words, and with clenched fist struck the man in the stomach.

The Hungarian slumped to the ground moaning. In staccato-like motion the officer kicked the wretch until Walter was sure the man would die on the spot.

"You will try to escape!" the officer shouted. "Swine!"

The man screamed and pleaded, but still the officer continued his brutal treatment until the sounds died to a whimper.

Walter wanted to turn his eyes away from the cruelty, but they seemed riveted to the scene. Sweat trickled down his cheeks as he silently prayed. "Oh, Lord, protect me. I am next."

When the officer had vented his rage on the hapless Hungarian, he stood over the victim panting and wiping his brow with the back of his sleeve. For a few moments he looked at the limp form at his feet. Then, straightening himself, he turned toward Walter and extended his right hand. This gesture came as such a surprise to Walter that he shook hands rather limply.

"My men have told me all about you," the officer said, and the faintest smile played in the corners of his mouth as he spoke. "None of us have ever heard anything like it." He glanced toward the two soldiers, who nodded their approval. "They've brought back a prisoner anyway, so they had a right to eat with you."

Walter started to speak, but his mouth went dry.

The officer smiled broadly. "For your kindness to my men you will have a holiday today. I shall make arrangements before sending you on."

It was truly a holiday of feasting for Walter. The officer assigned a German-speaking soldier to accompany him throughout the nearby village. While the officer was aware that Walter could speak Russian, he felt it would be better to have someone along who might bridge any communication gaps in case the complete story was not understood by the local citizens.

As Walter and the soldier made their way from house to house, everyone wanted to offer a token of appreciation by preparing food. At some places the Russian soldier phoned ahead so there would be no delay, but before long all the townspeople were aware that this escapee had a story to tell. Everyone enjoyed hearing the part telling how he shared his food with the soldiers, and they wanted to return the favor in their own way. Walter wished he could have saved some of the good things lavished upon him. It became such a progressive meal through town that by midmorning he was uncomfortably full.

The soldier had been ordered to escort Walter some miles eastward to a labor camp, and both men knew the effects of the prolonged feast would easily wear off by then.

Walter hated the thought of incarceration again, but he did not want to show ingratitude. As he stood by the gate of the labor camp and shook hands with the soldier, he smiled warmly. Off and on throughout the long day they had chatted in German, but now he deliberately spoke in Russian.

"I have appreciated this day with you," Walter said.

"It doesn't sound as if you needed me much." The soldier laughed, patting Walter's shoulder. "And I'm glad you had one day of feasting to the full."

"Good-bye," Walter said.

"Good-bye. You'll make out all right. There's only the slightest trace of a German accent."

"I came a long way without an interpreter."

The two shook hands again and waved a farewell.

While the camp was mainly a collecting point for those unfit for heavy labor, the new internee still had to undergo the usual belt confiscation and confinement procedure.

At the end of the week Walter was ready for further processing. The officers sent him first to the six-man barbershop for a complete beard and head shave. Next he took a sauna bath while his clothes were treated in the delousing ovens. He hadn't felt so clean since he entered Russia.

When he was told his first task, Walter smiled. "Thank you so much," he said.

The assigning officer looked puzzled. "Why do you thank me for a kitchen detail?"

"I like kitchen duty."

"Why?"

"That's where they keep the food, isn't it?"

The officer couldn't help laughing. People didn't usually thank him for work assignments, but he did see the point.

Walter busied himself peeling potatoes and singing to himself. He knew the Russians never overfed anyone in camp, but he could retrieve whatever scraps there were if he stayed close at hand.

Before long he spied another kitchen worker scraping the bottom of a kettle. The man was about to dump this into the garbage when Walter shouted to him. "Don't do that!"

The man looked up with a start. Walter was pointing toward him with the potato peeler.

"Why? I was told to scrape out all the burned things."

Walter shook his head. "I don't care who told you, don't do it. Keep those charred things. It's stupid to throw away good medicine."

The worker set the kettle down and went for the head cook. When he returned, the Russian at his heels was all frowns and ready for a fight.

"Why do you stop this man from dumping burned scrapings?"

Walter straightened himself and pushed his stool aside. "Anything burned like that can be used in diarrhea cases. Charcoal, anything like this, will work. It's good for all sorts of intestinal troubles."

"How do you know?" The cook put his hands on his hips.

Walter was about to relate his experience in the medical corps, but changed his mind.

"I just know, that's all. Try and see if it doesn't work."

They did try, and the word spread. Soon the camp authorities ordered the saving of all burned food and charcoal for medicinal purposes.

The camp learned of Walter's presence in other ways too. On the first Sunday he borrowed a balalaika from one of the Russians and shortly had the whole camp rollicking with folk music. Sitting in the center of the plaza, he played and sang for the prisoners while they joined in clapping and singing the tunes they loved so well. Throughout the whole time he punctuated the entertainment with selections from his own escape stories.

The next day a high-ranking officer approached Walter. His impassive face gave no clue to his real feelings, but Walter expected a reprimand for his Sunday's activities.

"I heard you play yesterday," the officer said.

Walter nodded.

"You play very well."

"Thank you. I tried to bring a little happiness. They need something to lift their spirits here."

"How would you like to play for the officers of this camp?"

"I would be glad to. I like to bring joy to anyone if I can," the prisoner explained.

The conscripted entertainer was made even happier when they rewarded him for his music with a full-course meal from the officers' mess.

As time went on Walter became so well-known in camp that wherever he went both prisoners and guards waved to him. He was transferred from the kitchen to the garage, where he worked as a mechanic on Russian motorcycles. He thoroughly enjoyed his new job and the continued prestige he had in camp, but always he wondered just when the next move should take place.

Just to be a popular prisoner was not his goal. Eventually he must move on, and timing was essential. There was the ever-present danger that the Russian authorities would piece together his stories and trace him to the original Makeyevka escape. He had consistently avoided any references to place names when recounting his escapes; but somehow, sometime, his records could catch up with him. If that ever happened, he would have a slim chance of ever reaching Berlin. He wished he hadn't been so eager to tell of all the providential leadings.

When the camp doctor came for a routine checkup at the end of the month, whole groups of prisoners were segregated for shipment. There was no rejoicing even though they were informed the train was going west. Too many rumors of entire contingents being sent to Siberia had been circulated to cause any happiness for those selected for the trip.

The officer, reading Walter Logé's name, stopped and frowned. "Step aside," he ordered.

Walter felt his blood run cold. He seldom was worried, but this time a wave of concern swept over him so rapidly he had little time to think. "It can mean only one thing," he thought. "They want me for hard labor."

For a week nothing further developed, and the strain of

silence bore down. Walter continued working at the garage, but all the time he fought worry and discouragement. It took an incident with another prisoner to change this pattern of thinking.

A German ex-soldier with one foot missing hobbled up to Walter one afternoon. "I've heard your stories," he said, "and I've been wondering. Are you a Christian?"

For a moment Walter was taken aback. He felt a quick sense of shame because his inner worry seemed to be showing. "Yes—yes," he stammered.

The man seemed to be searching Walter's eyes for a particle of courage. "I wish God would help me as He has you."

"Hasn't He?"

"I'm alive, anyway."

For a few minutes the two chatted amiably. When reference was made to home and family, however, the man's eyes grew moist.

"I thought maybe the Russians would ship me back to Germany when they saw I was crippled from the war," the man said, "but I've been in this camp six months." His voice broke. "I'm—I'm worried about—about my family."

"Worry is blind," Walter said, but he knew he was talking to himself as well. He put his tools down and gently took the man by the arm. "Let's go over to the barracks and pray."

In the quietness of the empty building Walter Logé prayed for this crippled stranger and his family. For a moment he forgot about his own problems while other thoughts flooded his mind. He thought of Alfred Mattern back at Makeyevka. What had happened to him? He suddenly remembered how low he had felt at Caracal, and the change that had come over him when he first met Alfred. The determination he had felt that day returned as he heard himself say again, "You can do anything if you set your heart to it." His jaw thrust forward in his characteristic manner as he silently prayed that he might retain that same courage.

"We need to watch and wait," Walter said half aloud. The words seemed more for himself than for the cripple. "In God's own time He will open the way to return."

The summer slipped away without further word about Walter's status. Then, suddenly, the whole camp was aroused in the middle of the night. Everyone was ordered on the line. Stumbling into the blinding glare of the floodlights, the prisoners milled about in crooked ranks not knowing why they had been forced from their bunks at one o'clock in the morning.

Walter edged closer as an officer read the names of those who would be shipped out. His name was not called on the first reading, but half an hour later he heard it when a new list was given. As the officer droned on, the procedure seemed endless. Men whose names had been called moved sleepily to the rear while the others pressed forward. Rumors ran the ranks in whispered tones, but no one knew exactly what was happening. Typically, the Russians had no intention of divulging their plans.

Three hours later those prisoners labeled for shipment were ordered to proceed to the train station several miles away. Weary from the walk after their nighttime wait, they dropped into the seats, relieved to be able to sit for a change. They were surprised to find the train already half loaded with prisoners transferred from other camps, some as far east as Siberia. The blending of the two contingents created a mixture of discussions about their destiny. It was a train loaded for a Romanian coal mine. No, they were being shipped to a copper mine in Siberia. They were headed for the Caucasus. The train was headed for the

West where they would all be sent home.

Walter could not satisfy his curiosity by simply listening to the prisoners. He got up and walked the length of the train to find the engineer. In one of the cars he recognized someone from Dnepropetrovsk. Quickly he glanced the other way for fear he would be detected. The last thing he wanted the Russians to have was an exact knowledge of his former whereabouts.

"It would be nice to renew an old labor-camp acquaintance," Walter thought as he pressed forward, "but the word could spread too easily."

At the front end of the first car Walter stepped from the train and made his way along the outside. Several guards were watching, but they recognized who it was and waved their approval.

Walter stood by the wheels below the cab and shouted to the engineer, "How long are you going to be here?"

A head appeared at the opening, and the engineer, surprised at being called, answered as if reporting to some superior officer. "Three hours."

"Thank you."

Turning away, Walter walked straight for the guards and asked permission to leave for the village bazaar.

One guard teasingly patted his rifle. "Just be back in time or we'll come and get you."

They all laughed. Walter had no intention of making an escape right then anyway. He had a hunch the train might go west, and he would like to get as much mileage out of the Russians as he could before slipping away again. At the moment he wanted to spend the last of his rubles for bread. Returning with several loaves, he shared these with some of the prisoners nearest him.

"You never know how often they'll feed us," Walter observed as he broke the bread.

This was the last solid food. From then on the Russians brought the prisoners nothing but cabbage soup twice a day. Guard replacements of men who were not so congenial and the constant surveillance of the passengers reminded them that they were still prisoners of war. Through long days and weary nights the train inched forward; but cattle cars were absent, and the general direction was westward.

On a miserable rainy day in late September they reached the end of the Russian line, where the track gauge changed. Ukrainian civilians were just unloading from an eastbound German-built train. The Soviets had promised these people free passage back to their homeland. They could bring back all their possessions accumulated in Germany while working for the Nazis, but their pro-German attitude was finally to catch up with them. At a time when they least expected it, the Russians demanded that they release all their belongings. Bicycles, luggage, boxes of clothes, baby buggies, and household things of every description—all were confiscated and placed in one heap.

The civilians, some sobbing, some dazed and silent, stood in the rain wondering what would happen next. A few had found temporary shelter under old pieces of scrap metal in the train yard. Children, frightened by the soldiers' presence, crowded close to their parents. Women clutched their crying babies while the men did what they could to comfort their families and to press the Russians for more information.

There were no answers. The soldiers intended to take all the valuable possessions of the repatriated Ukrainians.

Walter had no intention of waiting for orders. He knew enough of his captors' ways to realize that even after being told to transfer to another train they would have to wait for hours or even days before leaving. During the transfer of the prisoners he sauntered away toward the Ukrainian group and found a man with a mess kit.

"I'd like to borrow this," he smiled. "I'll bring it back after I eat."

The Ukrainian, thinking Walter was one of the soldiers, asked no questions, but he did seem puzzled by the last remark.

A thirty-five-man contingent of soldiers assigned to the railroad area had an army kitchen nearby, and Walter made his way toward it. The men had been milling about the tent, but were now lining up for chow as Walter sauntered over. Silently he stood in line and received a full army meal—no questions asked. Finishing, he washed the kit and returned it to the grateful, surprised Ukrainian.

Once Walter boarded the new train he wondered just how long he should stay with the prison unit. He knew it would be no great trick to escape. The guards never seemed too alert, and there were many stops which afforded easy movements away from the train. It was an ambivalent situation for him. He wanted to go by train as far as possible, but somewhere along the track the authorities might discover where he had been and send him back to a slave camp. In all the weary weeks they had been traveling, the Russians had never announced the destination nor what would happen to the prisoners when they got there. As the days wore on, Walter became edgy. To be slowly traveling in the right direction was not enough, and besides, it was high time to have something more solid than soup.

One afternoon when the train pulled into a Polish station, the pressure was too great. Within a few minutes after the rest stop, the hungry fugitive was down a side street making his way through this strange town.

Walter and Irma Logé in March, 1941, just before Walter's induction into the Wehrmacht. Walter wears his DRK (German Red Cross) uniform.

Mr. and Mrs. Logé pose with Dieter and Doris in July, 1944, when Walter was on leave from the front.

The Berlin apartment complex where the Logés lived at the close of the war.

Walter Logé in his Red Cross uniform as he prepared for a trip into occupied France.

Doris, Ursel, and Dieter on a visit to an aunt's country home in Sudetenland, July, 1944.

Tired German army truck drivers (Walter Logé at right) retire for the night.

Logé was assigned to the Bear Division's Second Medical Corps No. 257. Their first-aid stations they called "Bärenheim" (Bear Home), since all members came from Berlin.

The rapidly advancing Bear Division captured many pieces of Russian armor, such as these heavy tanks, and destroyed trains loaded with matériel. The Division's ambulances transported the wounded to military hospitals.

A depressing
sight in any war
—hundreds of
prisoners of war
awaiting an un-
certain future.

German soldiers,
aided by two
Russian boys, in-
spect a captured
tank.

Top: Ukrainians in their Sunday dress turn out to receive German troops.

Members of the 2d Medical Corps fraternize with Russian civilians during one of their stops.

A Russian peasant woman prepares a meal outdoors in the summer.

Near Slavyansk, USSR, horses and wagon became Walter Logé's supply vehicle after the trucks gave out in the mud and snow of winter.

Encircled German soldiers wave a welcome to a plane bringing supplies.

"Some of these sheep would make good food for German troops," the soldiers thought.

During an inspection at German Army Headquarters in Slavyansk, Walter Logé (sixth from left) was awarded the Kriegsverdienstkreuz (Distinguished Service Medal).

Logé (right) and a friend check the water in a country well.

As a result of the invasion of the Ukraine, long columns of weary prisoners marched westward to prison camps.

The winter in 1941 was severe, as usual.

Walter Logé displays the Distinguished Service Award (stripes on buttonhole).

Members of a platoon of the Bear Division pose for a group picture.

The Reserve Military Hospital, Landau, Southern Germany, where Logé was sent for care of his wounds and acute arthritis.

Certificate showing that Walter Logé was wounded in action on February 23, 1944.

BESITZZEUGNIS

DEM

Walter L o g é , Obgefr.

(NAME DIENSTGRAD)

2. San.Komp.(mot) 257

(TRUPPENTEIL DIENSTSTELLE)

IST AUF GRUND

SEINER AM 22. Februar 1944 ERLITTENEN

EIN MALIGEN VERWUNDUNG – BESCHÄDIGUNG

DAS

VERWUNDETENABZEICHEN

IN S C H W A R Z

VERLIEHEN WORDEN.

Im Felde . DEN 23. 2. 19 44

K. Fink

(UNTERSCHRIFT)

Oberstabsarzt u. Komp.=Chef

2.San.Kp.mot.257

(DIENSTGRAD UND DIENSTSTELLE)

Logé family picture taken in April, 1948. (The new baby, Reinhold, was born after the war, but did not survive.)

Irma's father and mother were among the first to meet Walter when he suddenly appeared in a Russian uniform.

Logé   Walter
(Name)   (Vorname)

Geboren am: 23.4.1911

Geburtsort: Berlin

Anschrift: Berlin-Zehlendorf

Zinnowweg 3

Dienststellung: Kraftfahrer

RK-Schwesternschaft:

RK-Bezirksstelle: Zehlendorf

RK-Bereitschaft m/w.: m.

Der Inhaber des Ausweises ist berechtigt, die Rot-Kreuz-Dienstbekleidung mit dem Abzeichen des „Roten Kreuzes" zu tragen. — Alle Behörden und Dienststellen werden gebeten, den Inhaber / die Inhaberin dieses Ausweises in Ausübung des Rotkreuzdienstes zu unterstützen und ihm / ihr jede Förderung angedeihen zu lassen.

(Eigenhändige Unterschrift)

Unterschrift der RK-Dienststelle

BERLIN. Dahlem

den 12.7.48

Walter Logé's identification as a part-time driver for the German Red Cross after his return to Berlin bears a picture reflecting some of the hardships through which he had passed.

The arrow (far right) points to the site of Walter's father-in-law's shoe store (with the shoe repair shop behind) where Walter suddenly appeared dressed in the Russian uniform. At the extreme right is the Zehlendorf station.

Irma Logé with Dieter and Doris in May, 1945, immediately after the war ended.

Peter Rijnbende (with Gertrude, on the occasion of their engagement).

Alfred Mattern, wounded officer Logé looked after in prison, as he appeared in Berlin in 1954.

A recent Logé family reunion in California. From left: Doris, Ursel, Irma, Walter, and David (formerly Dieter).

Walter Logé and the author, Jan Doward, examine a map of the escape route.

Walter, Doris, Irma, Ursel, and David as they appear today.

WALTER LOGE well remembered the first time he had walked through a Polish town. It had been shortly after the German massive eastern attack when the Russians were rapidly retreating. His outfit had just come within the city limits of a gutted area when they were forced to put their handkerchiefs to their noses. The whole place reeked with the stench of decaying flesh. Upon arriving at the shattered city hall, they discovered that the Russians had stacked the local dead cordwood fashion clear to the basement ceiling. Loath to handle the bodies, the Germans rounded up as many Jews as possible and forced them to dispose of the mess.

The Seventh Escape

Now, however, hunger pangs were steadily becoming so acute that they supplanted these repulsive memories of early war days in Poland. Walter walked about five miles before he stumbled onto the city hospital.

"They'll have food here for sure," the escapee said to himself. With the keen sense of smell known only to those long on an impoverished diet, he went straight to the basement and found the kitchen. Without an invitation he opened the door and walked toward the nearest cook. Now that he was outside the borders of the Soviet Union he felt it expedient to shift language gears.

"Sprechen Sie Deutsch?" Walter said.

The cook dropped his jaw simultaneously with the ladle in his hand. He whirled around to see who had entered the kitchen. Another cook hurriedly joined him, and the two crowded around Walter with their fingers to their lips.

"Shhhhhhh!" the two cooks whispered.

The cook nearest Walter looked pale as he whispered in German. "We're not supposed to speak German." He cast a quick glance toward the door and then back at Walter. "The Polish government will put anyone in prison for using the language."

Walter threw his head back and laughed heartily. "They won't put me in prison. I just came from there."

Quickly the ex-prisoner explained how he had escaped from the Russians and why he had come to the kitchen. The cooks could see how thin he was, but whether it was out of sympathy or because they feared his voice would carry, they hurriedly gathered up a sack and filled it with desserts and five loaves of bread. As Walter backed out of the kitchen he thanked the cooks again and again. They did not answer, but only nodded and smiled as they ushered him toward the door.

Once outside, Walter began to devour some of the sweet

bread while aimlessly wandering down the street. His immediate concern was easing the hunger pangs, but once these were satisfied he began to reflect on what he was attempting. On board the train he had felt anxious to be walking again, but now when he was full and free he wasn't too sure. As slow as the train traveled, it was better than walking. Home was a long way, but walking would make it even longer. Weeks, maybe months. Why should he spend needless energy on foot when the Russians provided a perfectly good train? This question kept recurring, and with every step he took, the advantages more and more seemed to outweigh the risks. Suddenly he stopped.

"It's worth a try," he decided. "Even if they find out where I have been I can slip away from them again. I know I can."

Retracing his steps, he finally arrived at the train station, but of course the train was gone. It had taken him over half a day to make his little round-trip escape.

At the far end of the station Walter saw five other prisoners who had missed the train. Two station officers had herded them together, where they huddled like frightened sheep in the corner. One of the officers was especially upset with a prisoner. Pacing back and forth in front of the cowering man he shouted, "I ought to punish you—send you to Siberia!"

Without hesitating Walter strode toward the officer. "Don't do that," he ordered. "I speak Russian. I will organize these men and take them to their train."

The officer, caught off guard, stared at Walter with surprise. "Well, who are you?"

"Walter Logé." Giving the officer no opportunity to ask further questions, he fired one of his own. "When does the next train come through here?"

"In five hours."

Walter smiled. "That won't make any difference. Any good train can catch up with that other one."

The station officer nodded. Apparently thinking Walter belonged to some supervisory group connected with prison exchange, he gladly turned the five men over to Walter and even arranged to have a meal brought to the men.

When the new train came, Walter boarded with his charges and explained to the engineer that he wanted to stop when they caught up with the prison train. He would have preferred to stay with the fast train, but the only way he could secure a ride was to deliver the prisoners.

Several hours later they easily made the transfer when they found the prison train waiting on a siding. Walter entered his old car swinging his bread sack while the five others found their places behind him.

"Where did you come from?" "How did you manage to get back?" "Where?" "How?" His friends wanted to know.

Walter sat down and opened his sack to share his acquisitions from the hospital kitchen. As he munched the bread with his friends, he recited the details of his last little excursion and concluded with one of his favorite texts:

"All things work together for good to them that love God."

During the last half of October, 1945, the autumn chill penetrated the unheated train. Regardless of their destination, everyone was anxious to be freed from the tedious trip, and with great relief they finally eased into their last stop, Frankfurt on the Oder.

Herded into an already overcrowded camp on the outskirts of the city, the newcomers joined others seated around small open fires in the compound. The only official word was an announcement that the new arrivals were under quarantine. From all Walter could gather this was a release camp where the Soviets intended to free those unfit for further service or prisoners best suited for propaganda reasons. He wished he could get out as soon as possible for fear his records might be found, but at the moment his body was too weary from riding, and he simply had to sleep. Curling up beside one of the fires, he lay down for several hours.

When he awoke, his mind was alert and ready to plan another escape. He was close enough to home to forget hitching rides. All he wanted now was an opportunity to slip away. For some reason the Russians had been very watchful of the prisoners when they arrived at the Frankfurt station. Walter began scanning the yard for possibilities, but he saw only the usual guard posts and barbed wire.

"If they have my case history, I'll be shipped back for sure," he fretted. "I must get away quickly. Three weeks is too long to wait."

Getting to his feet, he began circling the whole camp. At one end he found a dilapidated frame building alive with activity. Both Russians and prisoners were coming and going constantly.

Walter edged over to a man warming his hands by a fire. Holding his own hands over the heat, he casually began a conversation. "What goes on in the barracks?"

Without lifting his eyes from the fire, the prisoner answered slowly.

"That's where they give out the passports. Not the regular kind, but legal papers—enough to free a man."

"Who gets them?"

"Everybody who has spent three weeks here unless—" he hesitated while rubbing his hands together—"unless they suddenly change their minds and think you should go back to work."

Walter did not query further. He had heard enough. Turning his back on the fire, he warmed himself a few minutes more, then slowly walked toward the barracks. "I think I've come at the right time," he said to himself.

When he felt sure no guards were watching, he slipped inside. At the far end a short line of prisoners was formed in front of an inside window. Just as Walter made his way to the end of the line, the officer at the window called.

"How many more?"

"Ten," the last man answered.

"Eleven," countered Walter quickly.

The man wheeled around and faced Walter. "I didn't know you were there."

Walter didn't answer, but smiled pleasantly. "Now I know I've come on time!" he thought.

When Walter's turn came at the window, the officer did not bother to look up from his paper work.

"Name."

"Walter Logé."

"Spell it."

"L-o-g-é."

"Where are you going?"

"Berlin."

He was ready to volunteer his old street address, but there was no need for it. The Russian scribbled a few more notes and stamped a folded paper, pushing it with the tips of his fingers across the counter.

"You leave tomorrow."

Walter's heart pounded so loudly he was afraid the whole barracks would resound with the throbbing. He had used bold maneuvers before, but he felt this was his best. With supreme effort to control his voice, he spoke. "Thank you," he said.

It was closing time; officers were leaving, changes of

guards began milling about, and suddenly Walter found himself surrounded by Russians at a time when he felt like running. As casually as possible he made his way through the noisy barracks toward the remotest corner of camp. Finding a cluster of men seated around a fire, he squatted in their midst and made himself as small as possible. Fingering the folded paper in his pocket, he sighed to himself, "Whew! They're not as careful as I thought they'd be, but I don't want to tease them about it."

The Russians offered solid meals instead of the usual watery soup to everyone in the camp. It was obviously a propaganda demonstration before sending the men away, but when mess call was made Walter did not respond. Any other time he would have been in line, but now he was too excited and too afraid of being discovered.

"I'm free tomorrow," he kept saying to himself. "Tomorrow. It's too good to be true, though it is true. With a legal pass too!"

Tomorrow seemed remote. While the hours dragged by, Walter wandered aimlessly about, careful to keep as far away from Russian personnel as possible. Inwardly he was too edgy to talk to anyone. He avoided even those who had come with him on the train for fear they might discover he had the paper in his pocket. He fondled it hundreds of times to be sure it was still there. He was so close to home and yet so far away. Nothing wrong must happen now. Silently he prayed that he would be able to walk out the main gate without last-minute detection.

At three o'clock the next afternoon the loudspeakers blared: "Those holding passports will leave immediately through the main gate."

Walter reacted quickly. This time there was nothing casual about his movements. Crowding close to several who were hurrying toward the entrance, he held his pass for the gate officer to check. The happiest sound he ever heard was the final word as he left the camp.

"You are no longer under our control. Transportation will be provided from Frankfurt."

Free! Caught up in the excitement, Walter Logé was swept forward toward the station with those jubilant men who also had known slavery. Some hobbled on crutches, some were ill and staggered weakly, but all joyously moved toward their last Russian-sponsored train ride. Surely nothing could stay the tide of happiness, but for the men headed toward Berlin the train schedule seemed cruel. Their train did not leave until the next day!

Walter became edgy again. Another twenty-four hours and the authorities might find out what had happened. He paced the station platform, but the hours did not hurry.

"They could swoop down here at any time," he thought.

He was tempted to start walking, but each time he thought of that train going directly to Berlin he changed his mind. The ambivalent situation kept him awake most of the time until the train arrived and he fell exhausted into a seat.

Fortunately Walter could sleep the hours away, because what should have been a few hours' trip stretched into an all-night one. By four in the morning the train inched into the Berlin station. Even then no one could leave the train. Russian soldiers on a drunken spree were shooting up that section of the town, and the passengers had to wait until things quieted down. At last they unceremoniously left for their own sections. Some walked; some took the streetcars. But all scattered quickly.

When Walter tried to board a streetcar, the conductor looked at the soiled Russian clothes and lack of weapons. He shook his head. "You'll have to pay," he stated.

"I have just escaped from the Russians! I have no money at all."

The conductor smiled and beckoned Walter aboard. Turning around, he announced, "This man has just escaped from the Russians!"

The response was tumultuous. The people began plying Walter with queries about their own relatives.

"Have you seen my brother?" "I have a father in a slave camp; did you see him?" "My son was also captured. You didn't happen to find him, did you?"

Walter shook his head. "Russia is such a big place."

"Where do you live in Berlin?" someone asked.

"Zehlendorf Am Zinnoweg 3."

"Good! good! The American forces are in that sector."

Everyone wanted to have Walter talk, and he would gladly have accommodated them, except that other thoughts were racing through his mind just then.

Berlin, so gutted, so torn, so ravaged. He had not expected it so bad. Would he find Irma and the children alive? Now that he neared home his heart throbbed with real concern. If they had survived the bombings, what had happened when the Russians swept through?

The tracks were torn so badly that the trolley was forced to stop. All passengers going to Berlin-Zehlendorf transferred to the city train, the Stadtbahn.

"It will be just as well," Walter thought. "There's an S-Bahn depot across the street from my relatives' place."

As he picked his way through the rubble-strewn street toward the S-Bahn line his heart pounded wildly.

"If they're still alive, they'll know about Irma and the children—" His mind raced with his feet as he hurried between the great heaps of air-raid reminders.

When Walter alighted from the S-Bahn his heart leaped with excitement. Strangely enough, the building complex where his mother, aunt, and in-laws lived was still intact. Now he knew that someone, at least, must have survived.

His father-in-law ran a shoe-repair shop in the rear of a courtyard which formed an enclosure behind the apartments. Rather than go inside first, he rounded the corner of the building and headed for the shoe shop. He noticed a truck backed in the corner across from the shop. Several adults and children were unloading wood, but as they had their backs to him he didn't bother to speak.

Suddenly Walter felt one of his old teasing moods return. Barging into the shop, he called out boisterously in his best Russian, "Hello! How are you?"

Walter's father-in-law, busy nailing on a heel, did not look up at once. He continued working for a few moments longer. But when he raised his head and saw Walter grinning at him, the hammer did not make another blow.

Walter laughed heartily at the assortment of facial contortions which quickly ranged from alarm to unbelief to exuberance.

"Walter! Walter!"

Dropping his hammer, the older man ran around to the other side of the counter to embrace the ex-prisoner.

"We thought you were dead!"

Walter felt himself being hurried toward the door as his father-in-law shouted across the courtyard.

"Walter's back! Walter's back!"

Those unloading the truck looked up quickly. One man whom Walter had never seen before leaped from the truck and dashed down the street.

Then Walter was caught up in the excitement of greeting his relatives. Everyone talked at once.

"I recognized you the moment you came into the courtyard." His aunt laughed and pointed to an upstairs balcony. "I was up there dusting off my winter coat."

"I saw you from my window," his mother-in-law exclaimed, "but I thought you were a Russian coming after my husband!"

Walter threw back his head and laughed.

The happy chatter continued only a minute longer. Then Walter summoned all the courage he could and blurted out, "Irma—how are Irma and the children?"

"Fine, fine," his father-in-law said. "She's moved several blocks away now. That was Peter Rijnbende you saw leaving the truck. He's a Dutch refugee. He and his wife have moved in with us."

Walter was not listening. He started down the street in the direction his father-in-law had pointed. It was fine to fellowship with relatives, but suddenly all of his long-submerged emotions welled to the surface. He must see his wife. His mother and aunt joined him just to watch the reunion.

He was panting. The excitement of the past minutes, coupled with his loss of vitality, made his feet heavy as in a nightmare when limbs are leaden.

Suddenly Walter saw Irma coming. She was running—running toward him, face flushed, dark hair flowing, arms outstretched. Oh, God, how good to see her again!

Irma plunged into his arms. "Oh, Walter!"

They were dimly aware of relatives, bystanders who watched, but what matter? Time stood still as their hearts beat wildly in the thrill of reunion.

"My Jewel!" Walter whispered hoarsely.

Then he gently held her away and smiled. "Don't squeeze me too tightly. There's not much left."

Irma looked him up and down. "You are only a shadow of my Walter," she agreed. "I don't think you weigh a hundred pounds!"

Climbing the stairs to the apartment was a real struggle

for him. He had to use both hands on the railing to pull himself up. For a moment he stood on the landing by the doorway, breathing hard. Home! He had never lived in this place, but it was home now. He felt a rush of release in finally reaching his destination.

"It's a long road to freedom," he said slowly.

Irma looked into his tired eyes. In the quietness, away from the street, away from friends and relatives, alone for the first time, they began to pour out their hearts.

"I guess I'm selfish," Irma said softly, "but after Peter told me you were coming I hoped so much to greet you alone. It just seemed that—"

"It doesn't matter," Walter smiled. "We're together now."

"I know it doesn't, not really. Yet, after waiting those long months when I didn't know whether you were alive or dead—" She looked at the floor, then looked again into his eyes. "Father said I should forget about you, that it was useless to hope, the way the war was going. He said to go ahead and remarry as soon as I could."

Walter started to speak, but Irma quickly continued.

"I didn't give up hope, Walter—never, even when there was no word. I prayed and believed. I only asked that God would sustain me."

Walter smiled fondly at his wife. "So many times I could see your face. It beckoned me on. When I arrived in Berlin, though, I was frightened. I couldn't know if you were still alive."

"Our old apartment was too close to the center of town, so we moved. But toward the last it didn't matter anyway. The Allies bombed night and day." Irma's voice was strained; the memory was still fresh. "Our old apartment was bombed shortly after we moved, and three people were killed. It was awful, Walter. Most of the time there were no lights or gas, and near the end they didn't even have air-raid warnings. We did not undress for a month, but God was so good to us. Not even a scratch in spite of everything."

Walter had seen enough war to visualize the terror by day and by night. Then he spoke slowly, deliberately. "What happened when the invading army came through?"

"The first time I saw them it really scared me. I had just stepped outside when I saw two of them coming from the house next door—coming right for me. I wanted to run, but then I remembered what you had told me."

Walter smiled. "Never act afraid of them. Talk loudly."

Irma nodded. "I did not have to talk, though. I just stood there and faced them. They looked me all over and then the apartment, but finally they moved on. The next night was worse, though." Her voice trailed off almost to a whisper. "It was terribly frightening."

She told him how the troops had found the wine cellar beneath the city hall and then spread out through the whole area, block by block, door to door, rough, uncouth, bestial. They seized watches, jewelry, and females. It mattered little about the latter's age or condition. They took what they wanted and moved on.

"I was determined to keep myself clean, Walter. They could have everything but my body and my children." She paused and cleared her throat. "It was a miracle that they did not find us. They kicked at the basement entrance and then came stomping down the stairs where we were staying at night. Several families of us shared the basement for protection, and the neighbor's door was ajar, hiding the entrance to our little room. The soldiers took valuables from the old people, but did not hurt them. Best of all, they left without ever finding us behind the other door."

Irma gave a little chuckle. "I was so afraid they'd hear my heart pounding."

She reached over, took Walter's hands in hers, and smiled. "Now that will be enough for this time. I'll tell you later how we sang through all the air raids and how well Dieter and Doris behaved. Right now I'd better get something for you and the children to eat."

"The children! Where are they?" Suddenly he realized that he had walked right by them in his father-in-law's courtyard. A few minutes later Dieter and Doris came bounding up the stairs full of happy chatter about their getting to ride on the truck to haul firewood. As Walter hugged them both, he felt now that he was really home again.

"But where's Ursel?" he wanted to know.

Irma paused a moment while putting on her apron. "Walter, I don't know exactly. When she became so afraid of the bombings I took her to her aunt's in Czechoslovakia. That was last winter. It seemed a good idea because she could be in the country and go to school. I intended to go back and get her in a few weeks, but travel restrictions came in February, and I haven't heard from her since. I've been praying so much for her. The Russians have not permitted any contact, and certainly the Czechs have no special love for Germans."

There was a long silence. Finally Walter spoke. There was a familiar ring to the confidence in his voice. "She'll be back. The Lord will guide her. All we can do now is wait and pray."

Irma took his cue and said cheerfully, "Now just as soon as our daddy changes his clothes we can have something to eat." She turned up her nose in exaggerated disgust. "Those Russian things will all have to be burned. I want no animals in here."

Walter laughed. "I haven't been too lonely with these lice. They've kept me company a long time."

"Too long!" Irma agreed.

Irma had few provisions for a full-scale celebration, but she did manage to boil a kettle of potatoes. She stepped out of the kitchen to see that the children washed their hands, but by the time she returned Walter had eaten all the potatoes.

There would be other times when they could celebrate more fully. Three months later the Russians released Alfred Mattern as unfit for labor. Years would pass before he could walk without crutches, but his determination eventually triumphed. Later even Sister Gerda came home. Broken in health but not in courage, she too found a new life. Eventually they located Walter and had their own happy reunion.

Walter was shocked to learn what had happened after he vanished from Makeyevka.

"They gave me the water treatment," explained Sister Gerda.

Walter leaned forward. "You?" he asked.

"They needed a scapegoat, I guess. Remember, I took care of you briefly in their so-called hospital just before you escaped. They thought I knew something about your plans and made me stand in cold water to my neck for hours, day after day for a whole week."

"And she nearly died," added Alfred.

Walter tried to speak, but the words would not come.

Sister Gerda waved her hand slightly as she smiled. "Don't worry. The price was high, but even at the time I secretly hoped you'd make it all the way to Berlin. Now I know it was worth it."

By the end of July, 1946, Ursel's stay at her aunt's finally ended. She was released at the camp in Schlotheim,

Thuringia, after much difficulty and red tape. Her arrival brought the whole family together in the biggest celebration of all.

After eight more years Walter was able to fulfill another dream, when he brought his family to America to start life over again. The children have now received their education and settled in southern California, while Walter and Irma remain in Michigan.

Reunions are still occasions of great joy for the Logeś. Irma and the children have their own stories to recount of God's protecting hand over them. But when Walter retells the story of his seven escapes and his epic flight across the vast Russian territory, it brings new thrills every time. Whether he recalls some incident never mentioned before or describes a familiar scene, his successful return to home and loved ones will ever evoke deepest feelings of admiration and gratitude.